DENIAL

MORRISSEY

Britain's Next
BESTSELLER

First published in 2015 by:

Britain's Next Bestseller
An imprint of Live It Publishing
27 Old Gloucester Road
London, United Kingdom.
WC1N 3AX

www.britainsnextbestseller.co.uk

Copyright © 2015 by Jamie Jones

The moral right of Jamie Jones to be identified as the author
of this work has been asserted by him in accordance with the
Copyright, Designs and Patents Act 1988.

All rights reserved.

Except as permitted under current legislation, no part of this
work may be photocopied, stored in a retrieval system,
published, performed in public, adapted, broadcast, transmitted,
recorded or reproduced in any form or by any means, without
the prior permission of the copyright owners.

All enquiries should be addressed to Britain's Next Bestseller.

ISBN 978-1-910565-23-0 (pbk)

For FLJ

CHAPTERS

1990

1991

1992

1993

1994

1995

1996

1997

1998

1999

INTRODUCTION

27th November 1995, Cardiff International Arena.

Reach up.

Reach your hand up.

Reach your hand up and he will take it.

Reach your hand up and he will take it and you'll have done it.

I KNOW that all I have to do is pull my arm out of the crush that is fast enveloping me and he will haul me up onto the stage. We've established the required eye contact, he sings the line detailing rumours that keep him grounded whilst looking at me, as he ponders why I'm not reaching my hand up further to clasp his. This is my chance, I know that. This is my chance to take my rightful place up on that stage like so many before me have done. This is the time for my 19 year old childlike frame to step up onto that stage and to embrace him.

It's him, I have to do this now. All those hours spent in my bedroom, howling to 'Speedway' have led to this moment. Just do it, don't worry about your glasses falling off or not being strong enough to scramble onto the stage, just do it.

Why won't my hand move?

Hesitation is never a winning option in such momentous situations but I can't do it, I can't reach up. My pulsating brain has lost control of my limbs and the utter perfection of getting up there to that song has caused a system meltdown. This is my sick way, it could change everything, I've dreamt about it and now it's here, I can't do it.

I've been here since 2pm, waiting for the doors of the arena to open so that I could run to the stage barrier with the other diehards, whilst the hordes wander and mutter, uninterested in what he has to sing.

No time to reminisce, this is happening now, in front of me, I can't wait.

And that's it, he's sung of strange, sick ways and the truth and it's over. He's just looked at me like I was insane for not taking my chance and he's right.

Now I need to slink away, make way for the next batch of desperate, sweaty youths who won't waste their chance when it arrives.

I will never make the stage, that urge within will never be satisfied and even when Moz tried to help me, I couldn't help myself.

1990

Changes

IT'S easy to blame my dad. For the first 13 years of my life I wasn't really interested in anything other than football and Star Wars, with occasional breaks to watch Grange Hill and The Dukes of Hazzard.

Then Dad decided to introduce me to music.

On 26th March 1990, I found myself at the Docklands Arena sat in front of a figure that would change my life forever, and my dad. I wasn't even meant to be at that David Bowie gig. My mum was an avid 1970's Bowie fan and was due to attend with my dad so that they could re-live their youth, but fell ill on the day of the gig. As he couldn't find any of his mates that fancied going, Dad decided to take me. He didn't ask me if I wanted to go, he made the decision for me. He had a spare ticket that he had shelled out £17.50 for and he wasn't going to waste it whether I wanted to go or not.

In the car on the way down to London, I treated it like a big adventure, heading off to my first concert, and to what Dad always referred to as "The Big Smoke". During the journey, Dad fed various David Bowie tapes into the stereo and began to regale me with tales of seeing Elton John and Bowie live in the 1970's. I'm not even sure he was concentrating on the traffic when, misty-eyed and wistful, he began to quietly repeat "Those were the days..." I snapped him out of his trip down memory lane by asking if he also liked to dress like Bowie and Elton back in the 70's? At this point he refocused on the road and his inner heterosexual, working class man came racing to the surface and he dismissed me with a curt; "Don't be so bloody stupid".

He then asked me what Bowie songs I knew, but the only one that I could recall was "Dancing In The Street", the single that he released with Mick Jagger where the two of them appear to be having a pouting competition in the video. Dad was not impressed with my knowledge and rambled on about how Bowie would play all his hits as part of the "concert", and that I should be grateful for having been given the ticket. I wasn't overly excited as we reached the venue which, from the outside, looked nothing more than a huge warehouse in the middle of east London.

We dutifully queued to hand over our tickets and made our way inside the cavernous arena. We found our seats, which were only about 20 rows from the front, just as the house lights were dimmed and Bowie took to the stage. Even with one of his musical heroes being only 30 yards away, Dad didn't stop grumbling about the price of the bottle of Pepsi that I'd persuaded him to buy me from the concessions stand. As the crowd roared its approval, Bowie sang the opening lines of "Space Oddity" and I felt like I had been kicked squarely between the legs. This amazing noise and retina burning flash of lights was a revelation, a miracle happening in front of my eyes. Instinctively, I went to stand up and dance before being hauled back to my seat by Dad, who was gently shaking his head.

In a blizzard of style, panache and power, Bowie paraded across the length of the stage and I sat in my seat open-mouthed. I was spellbound by this beautiful middle-aged man with a voice that could shatter glass from half a mile away.

Who knew that Bowie was this good? Why had nobody told me before?

I hadn't found any women attractive up to that point of my life, (aside from Belinda Carlisle, naturally) let alone any men. Men in 1980's pop music had been either dressed as badly made-up women (Boy George/Robert Smith), like the young men who worked for the local insurance company (Rick Astley) or were just strange (Morrissey). Here was Bowie, the thin white duke, and I adored him from the moment I set my bespectacled eyes upon him.

It turned out that I did know plenty of Bowie songs. Tunes like "Changes" and "Life On Mars?" had become such a part of popular culture that I'd heard them numerous times on the radio or the TV but just hadn't associated them with him. I was loving the show, as were the rest of the crowd who were producing an electric atmosphere inside the arena. I had been to football matches and witnessed the fans playing a part in the main event but this was different. Here, the crowd were desperate to show their devotion. All around us were men in Bowie t-shirts, screaming their love for the man on the stage, much to Dad's obvious discomfort.

The whole crowd going absolutely bonkers as Bowie rattled through "Heroes" caused such a reaction deep in my adolescent chest that I wasn't sure if I was having a heart attack or was about to wet myself. During the quieter numbers, most of the crowd in this enormodome sat quietly watching Bowie glide across the stage, but two rows in front of us was a woman who refused to sit down. She had a sharp Ziggy Stardust style haircut and danced with a crazed, hazy look in her eyes – the same kind of look that lads got on their face after their mates have spun them round 20 times in the playground. When Dad spotted me staring at her, he said: "Just ignore her, she must be on something!". On something? I had no idea what he meant. The only thing I knew you could be "on" was the god-awful banana flavoured medicine that was used to kill all known childhood illnesses in the 1980's. She was as captivating as Bowie despite her age, which was probably about 25. I spent the rest of the show alternating between watching Bowie and sneaking furtive glances at her. Both were provoking an odd, warm feeling deep inside me that I'd never felt before. Even before the gig ended, I had promised myself that I would do everything in my power to experience such feelings again in the near future.

I left my seat buzzing from the energy of the show and the crazy dancing of the Ziggy Stardust woman. I was brought back to earth when, despite my boundless enthusiasm, Dad refused to buy me a tour t-shirt due to them being "12 pounds soddin' 50, they must be joking!" He then completed my comedown by spending the next twenty minutes saying that Bowie had been, 'Ok I suppose, but not as brilliant and bloody life changing as you are making out", before reminding me that gigs were much better in the 1970's.

Some kids would have used the inspiration of such a life-changing gig to think: "I want to write songs or be in a band". I didn't, I thought "Fuck me – live music is superb". I sat in the car, annoying Dad with my relentless adrenaline fueled splutterings about gigs and Bowie. He answered a few questions but after about an hour of the journey said that he'd heard enough of Bowie for the night and put on his new Genesis tape. That just provoked me to ask him if Phil Collins was still a miserable bald tosspot when he played live? In return I got a clip round the ear and a sly chuckle.

I went home to Peterborough and dwelt in my bedroom for the next couple of days, listening to all of my parents music collection. In amongst the Pink Floyd and Whitney Houston CD's, I would find the odd gem like Tracey Chapman's debut album which I then proceeded to play until I knew all of the words. I would go up to my room after tea and listen to the indie and rock songs that were being played on our local radio station during the impeccable "Jive Alive" show. The DJ's, Mick and Sarah Jane, would introduce a song and I would rush to press play and record on my tape deck. Even if it was a song I didn't particularly like, I needed to record it, listen to it and drink it in. I had caught the music bug.

In order to see if I could look like Bowie (or indeed any other androgynous space-rock being), I had a quick dabble with Mum's make-up. I ended up looking more like George, the effeminate hippo from Rainbow, than Bowie or Bolan. I did though make some space on my bedroom wall, amongst the Star Wars and Peterborough United posters, for a postcard of Bowie in full Ziggy Stardust regalia. It felt like I had taken a huge step towards the almost mythical status of being 'grown up'.

Peterborough, My Peterborough

THIS story begins in my home city of Peterborough. To be honest, the spectacular Norman Cathedral aside, it isn't much to look at. My view of the old place is undoubtedly skewed by my love for Peterborough United, otherwise known as 'The Posh'. Since my grandad first took me to watch them in 1983 at their ramshackle London Road ground, as a 6 year old, I've been addicted.

Peterborians tended to be miserable, moaning gits who are very much in the "glass half-empty" camp. I fitted in perfectly.

Up until 1989, my nuclear family had lived in an area of the city called Stanground. I had a terrific time growing up there, mainly because we had lots of playing fields for football and all my mates lived within a few hundred yards of our house. Ok, so some of the locals that you saw hanging around the parade of shops or outside the pubs weren't the greatest but as long as you kept your bike close by you could make a quick enough getaway.

We lived in an ex-police house which had a huge garden, ideal for football and re-enacting scenes from Return Of The Jedi. Dad even built me an aviary in the back garden, so that I could spend hours out there looking after our greenfinches and quails. As a geeky young kid, some of my happiest moments were spent sat on the floor of that aviary with my friends, the birds, flying and walking all around me. I fought like Frank Bruno (gallantly but ultimately unsuccessfully) to stay in that house. Alas, even the whining of their 13 year old son couldn't stop my parents from climbing the social ladder. Mum and Dad both had the hangover from the 1980's Thatcher bug that had engulfed dear old England and wanted to "better themselves". So, we moved out of the centre of Stanground and onto a new housing development which was located just 300 yards from my secondary school. The one bonus to the dreaded move was that the new house had a spare room, which I quickly colonised into my own. After seeing Bowie, I would spend unending hours wedged under the wooden desk in that room, trying to find some peace and quiet in which to listen to music and contemplate the meaning of life. Under that desk was my favourite place in our house, it was my space, a spot to hide away and call my own. I would lay under there and write my thoughts on the underside of the desk, knowing that nobody but me would ever see them.

My mum and dad had been childhood sweethearts who'd split up after they left school, before making their way back to each other a few years later and getting married. They created for me, and latterly my sister, a loving, stable household. We all got along pretty well, albeit with the usual family ups and downs. Some days in our house it would resemble Prime Ministers Questions with everyone trying desperately to get their points across above the noise, but at the end of the day we would generally sit down and watch Neighbours together.

I'm 5 years older than my kid sister Erika, and from the day she was born she has been the princess of our family. I was as bad as my parents. When she was a small child anything she wanted, if I could get it for her, I would. As a toddler, she didn't need to learn how to toddle; I would push her round in her walker like some kind of baby royalty.

Dad was always happy with his own company and wouldn't waste words by gossiping or talking when he didn't need to. He played me the first song that I remember hearing regularly which was "Captain Beaky & His Band". A song that Dad would put on his record player for me then change the names of Beaky's band to fit in my name, much to my annoyance.

From Captain Beaky I eventually moved on to buying my own music. For years I told anyone that asked that "Do They Know It's Christmas?" was the first single that I bought with my own money. However, that single was released in 1984 when I was only 8. Unless Woolworths accepted Panini football stickers in exchange for 7" singles, I am pretty sure Mum must have brought that single for "the house" and I borrowed it at some point and created a memory out of it.

In reality, my first purchase seems to have been an unusual piece of good taste for a 10 year old. For Christmas 1986 I bought Dexys Midnight Runners "Because of You" on 7" vinyl as a Christmas present for a girl called Grace at my junior school. In an entirely innocent way, Grace was my first girlfriend in so much as we got on ok, but we spent the vast majority of our time ignoring each other and hanging around with our friends. In return for this excellent gift, Grace bought me "Caravan of Love" by The Housemartins, which was also a cracking tune. So my first instance of music and the opposite sex hadn't gone too badly. It was a fleeting romance, but we both got a magnificent 7" single out of it.

From Mum, I picked up many things including pathological stubbornness and the ability to never give up on an argument even when you know you are in the wrong. This was to be a personality trait that was to play a big part in how I grew up.

Music wasn't a constant in our house. None of us could play an instrument but it was never far away, whether that be Steve Wright on Radio 1 in the car, or Mum playing her Harry Chapin records in the dining room. From such humble beginnings and without ever having formally invited it in, music was about to take over my life.

Becoming a Braggist

NOT only did that Bowie gig spark a new found passion for music, it also triggered my youthful hormones and I began to notice the girls at our school for the first time. I had always known they were there but I was far too busy with the aforementioned Peterborough United and Star Wars to pay close attention. After I turned 14 in the summer of 1990, it felt like everywhere I looked there were lumps, under ever tightening school jumpers, and gloss encased lips catching my attention. The gentle stirring in my loins inspired me to attempt to make an emotional and possibly physical contract with a girl by 'asking her out'. The good looking girl I had begun to fancy also had the added attraction of being the only female supporter of The Posh in the whole school. Her name was Jo, and the fact that she owned the same England 1990 World Cup shell-suit as me made it seem that our getting together was written in the stars. Jo was an attractive girl with long blonde hair who, despite us being in the same class, was nearly a full year older than me and was a very worldly wise 15 years of age. She was a qualified lifeguard so was very fit and had the confident attitude to the world that, to my boyish eyes, all teenage girls seemed to possess.

The loosely applied school uniform rules allowed girls such as Jo to leave blouse buttons undone, fold over the waistbands on their skirts after they had left their mothers protective gaze and sport a look that made them look much older than us mere boys. I was amazed she agreed to the offer to go out with me. I didn't have much to offer her in terms of personality, and my NHS specs and floppy brown hair hadn't exactly had the girls running to my front door. Our coupling had been inevitable once I'd stolen her rucksack and she'd run after me as I half-heartedly made my attempted escape. As part of my strategy, I let her catch up with me behind the science block, where, stumbling over my words I asked her if she would go out with me? With only a moment's hesitation, she advised me that she wanted to take up my offer and with a quick peck on the lips our union was secured.

After seeing Bowie, I had quickly developed a mild addiction to the work of the Scottish rockers, Deacon Blue. I'd heard their single 'Dignity' on Radio One, taped it and couldn't stop playing it. It was a story about a man saving up for a boat (called Dignity), which didn't exactly resonate with my life but Ricky Ross' husky, storytelling voice had me hooked. Having heard the single a hundred times, I persuaded Mum to buy the CD version of the album from which it came, "Raintown". I was hooked from the first listen. It was the first time that I had experienced that incomparable rush of excitement and adrenaline when you put on an album and it instantly takes over your life, making everything else other than the songs contained within its sleeve seem utterly pointless.

I also developed my first serious crush, on Ricky Ross' co-vocalist (and I was to discover, wife) Lorraine Mcintosh. Whilst my mates were grasping their youthful hormones and gazing at pictures of Cindy Crawford, for me it was all about Lorraine.

I don't know if it was a conscious decision, but I knew with absolutely certainty that it was my romantic mission to indoctrinate Jo into the magical musical landscape created by Deacon Blue.

They had some top tunes for a young couple who were just discovering emotions, kissing and politics, and 'Raintown' was our album of choice that summer. Well, I say ours, but I can only hope that Jo liked it as well, as I didn't ever really check. To figure out what a girl was thinking or what she liked was way outside of my emotional range.

World events came thick and fast in 1990, whether that be the start of the Gulf War or my becoming mesmerised by both the tune to Beats International's sublime 'Dub Be Good To Me' and Lindy Layton's dancing in the video. Jo and I would talk about such events, though not so much about my growing fondness for Ms Layton as Jo was the jealous type. In essence "going out" with each other was just a phrase that people used, we didn't actually go to many places. Occasionally we would sit together in French class, much to the amusement of my mickey-taking mates and hold hands under the desk. She would write things like "Jo Loves Jay" on my wallpaper covered exercise book and I would put a functional tick next to it. I had no idea what else to do and she seemed happy with my formal approval. In the next break time, I would cross through her declaration of love with a black marker pen. I couldn't risk my mates seeing such naked teenage emotion.

Every Wednesday after school I would get the bus over to hers to sit and listen to music and she would take the short walk from school to my house to do the same every Monday. She was far smarter than me, both intellectually and in the ways of the world. Immediately prior to our starting to go out she had been seen out and about with one of the 16 year old lads at our school who had a moped. The moped was the ultimate status symbol of the callow youth looking to impress girls from 2 or 3 school years below them. The rumour in the playground was that he finished with her for being frigid. That word was used a lot by my peers but I didn't really have a clue what it meant. I didn't know much about relationships, or life outside of the school gates and our front room. I was still wearing my favourite Indiana Jones pants to school on non-PE days.

Jo helped me find out more about life by insisting that we go for a walk every Monday evening. We would inevitably end up in a secluded, darkened corner round the back of the deserted school science block. There we would spend an hour, often in the pouring rain or freezing cold, kissing and fumbling our way into the next stage of our lusty quest to reach maturity.

Bowie and Jo had changed my immature boy's mindset. I was moving away from posters of Ninja Turtles and Wookies to walls full of pop stars. I wasn't so interested in watching the likes of Newsround and Blue Peter anymore and, instead, was often sneakily setting up our video recorder to tape the late night film on Channel 4.

Slap bang in the middle of that glorious summer came the World Cup. It's hard to put into words how much Italia '90 changed the way that people viewed football in England. Well, I knew nothing of England as a whole, but it certainly changed views in my 5 square mile home patch of Southern Peterborough. Thanks to Thatcher demonising football fans and the disasters at Heysel and Hillsborough, if you showed an interest in football prior to that World Cup, you were naturally assumed to be a hooligan by most people. My mum had always sniffily said to her friends: "Yes, Jay goes to watch the football, but he doesn't ever get into trouble and we are hoping he will grow out of it".

The World Cup that year even changed how Mum thought about football. It was a tournament littered with poor England performances in the early rounds but thanks to Gary Lineker's goals v Cameroon, England were through to the semi-final. Everything was set up perfectly as far as I could see for that "Night in Turin" and the game against West Germany.

My dad had never been that keen on football. In fact his only interest in the beautiful game was to wind me up about defeats for The Posh and to hide the local daily paper from me so that I couldn't get the up to date(ish) football news. I had my revenge by ringing the premium rate Club Call line to get my football news fix, thus sending our phone bill through the roof. Dad would walk around the house ranting about the bill and how he "only used the phone in emergencies". British Telecom ruined that particular scam when they introduced itemised billing.

On the evening of the semi-final, Dad came home from work talking about how much he was looking forward to the game. Of course, he showed his inner-Peterborian by informing me that he was, "Sure we will lose". With our tea and the washing up dispatched by 6.30pm as well as my mum and sister packed off to watch TV upstairs, Dad and I settled down in our front room with a mug of sugary tea each. I was resplendent in my blue England kit, full of hope that we would win the match and go on to win the World Cup. What could possibly go wrong? I instinctively knew that this was going to be a special night in our house; we would soon be celebrating a win that would be remembered for years to come.

As it was a warm night, we had our front room windows wide open and could hear the shouts and squeals as our neighbours watched the game. At least, I hope that's what they were doing.

I howled at the screen when West Germany opened the scoring and knocked the lampshade off the big light when Lineker bundled home the equaliser. I gripped Dad's arm as tightly as I could to avoid crying along with Gazza when he was booked, and hardly noticed as Dad prattled on nervously about cheating and two World Wars and one World Cup. After an emotionally exhausting 90 minutes and then extra-time, the score was 1-1, and the game was set to be resolved by a penalty shootout. I was quite relaxed at this point as I remained convinced that we would win. It had been 24 years since the greatest country on the planet had won the World Cup, so it stood to reason that it was going to happen now. I stuck on my England/New Order's anthem "World in Motion" record, and screamed along at the top of my voice to John Barnes rap about being the "England man". It occurred to me, for the first time, that all might not go to plan when Dad came into the front room carrying his 30th cup of tea of the night and announced "I'm going out into the garden, I can't watch this. Shout me as the penalties are taken, I'll leave the door open".

Both sides scored their first 3 penalties with consummate ease. Walking up to take our next spot kick was Stuart Pearce. As an emotionally stunted juvenile, you couldn't be certain of many things in life but walking across my TV screen was one of those certainties in the shape of Stuart Pearce. I knew that he would score. He was Psycho. He was the ultimate Englishman. He was England.

He missed.

Some moments in any young life are frozen in time, and that was one.

"SHHHHHIIIIITTTTTT, SHHHHIIITTTTT........ DAAAAAAAAAAAAAAD.......NNNNNOOOOOOOOOOOOOOOO".

As Dad ran back into the house, I knew that he was caught up in the moment because he didn't clip me round the ear for shouting "Shit" out of our front door. He put his arm around my shoulder and we stood and watched in silence as West Germany scored their next penalty. Next up for England was Chris Waddle who sprinted to the ball and then blasted it high into the warm Italian night. England were out of the World Cup.

I threw myself onto the floor in a melodramatic mess of tears, snot and smeared specs. Dad picked me up with his shovel sized hands and gave me a hug. My dad was a typical working class man and, in 1990, working class dads only gave their kids a hug if they'd had a limb amputated. I sat there weeping into his shoulder, thinking about how crap life was and knowing without doubt that I would never be this upset about anything, ever again. I eventually went up to bed, still blubbering and refusing to take off my England kit. I cried myself to sleep muttering to the end about how unfair everything was.

In the midst of my World Cup heartbreak, I realised that the tunes of Deacon Blue and the Blow Monkeys (who had become my 2nd favourite band) were not enough to heal this kind of pain. I needed something raw, something real, something exciting. The songs on Radio 1 were saying nothing to me about my life so I had no idea where I would find such musical enlightenment. It didn't happen immediately but later that summer, playing through our car stereo, sat outside my Nan & Grandads caravan on a wet Cromer afternoon, I found what I was searching for. I found a voice that sounded like a barking seal and a guitar sound that resembled a mallet hitting a plank of wood. I found Billy Bragg.

Rather than joining in with a family game of Cluedo, I sat in our sky blue Ford Escort and rifled through the cassette tapes that I had liberated from the glove box. After a quick blast of Madonna's "True Blue", I found a tape that had a cover upon which was a huge cartoon head with a furnace as the mouth, and a hand scooping money into it. The cover had on it the words "Billy Bragg – Talking With The Taxman About Poetry" and a sticker that said "Pay No More Than £3.99". As most shops were charging £7 for a tape, my first thought was, "What an idiot this bloke is for not wanting to make more money".

I hadn't been that interested in politics up to this point. My dad had recently been made redundant from his job at a local factory and had struggled to find another job for a while. Despite that, my dear Mother had caught the 80's bug and desperately wanted to be middle class. As a small child, we lived in a house that had an outside toilet. Between smashing my football against the fence and pretending that the trees in our garden were the Endor forest, I liked the fact that I could nip for a quick wee without having to take my shoes off and go inside. Mum had other ideas though. How could she be aspirational middle class with our own car, hi-fi stereo with graphic equaliser and still have an outside toilet? The toilet door was soon locked, never to be opened again. My mum was a gigantic pile of confusing contradictions. She was desperate to join the middle classes but would also stand in our kitchen screeching along to Billy Bragg's left wing political anthems with her distinctively awful singing voice.

'Talking With The Taxman...' was a delectable mix of Billy telling stories, with songs about his lack of desire to tie the knot (The Marriage), and the "I'm an idiot and she left me" love-song (Honey, I'm a Big Boy Now). The political ram-raid named "Ideology", wandered over and smacked me full in the face. It made me sit up and take notice of the world around me, rather than just concentrate on me and mine. In the song, Billy doesn't seek to deliver a complicated message or dress up the meaning in fancy words; it's raw, almost primal language.

I sat in the car and listened to that tape 5 or 6 times all the way through, finding a different song to fall in love with each listen. I knew that from hereon in it was me and Billy against the world. He had given me a blueprint of how life should be lived, both politically and in affairs of the heart. I was primed to listen to anything and everything that he had to say. From that day onwards I told people that I was a socialist, but in reality I was a Braggist.

I spent the next week listening to that album on constant repeat before it snapped and I knew I needed to go out and get some more Bragg tunes.

I had a few record shops to choose from. We had the expensive (HMV and Our Price), the old style independent (Andy's Records) and the hippy run 2nd hand haven that, in Peterborough, was called House On The Borderland.

Our Price was always my first point of call. That wasn't an effort to be cool or trendy; it was just the closest record shop to the bus station.

I now knew that Billy Bragg had insisted that all his albums had the "Pay No More Than....." sticker on the front cover. However, as I made my way to the CD racks, I found that the management of Our Price, being good capitalists, weren't going to pay any attention to this socialist nonsense. There in the rack sat Billy's "Workers Playtime" album with a dirty great £13.99 sticker proudly displayed on the cover.

I couldn't afford such an outrageous price. I only had £9 in my pocket, and that had been scraped together from my £3 a week pocket money and my Sunday paper round which paid a measly £1.50 a week. Due to these financial pressures, I was lucky to be able to afford one album a month, so it had to be the right one and at the right price.

With my face set to maximum smugness, I approached the seemingly 7ft high counter with "Workers Playtime" in hand, and said to the bloke behind it:

Me – 'You can't charge £13.99 for this CD!'

Him – 'You what?' (customer service was universally awful in 1990)

Me – 'You can't charge £13.99 for this CD!'

Him – 'Shop policy is that we charge that for obscure CD's.'

Me – 'Obscure? This is a Billy Bragg album.'

Him – 'Yes mate and you're the only one that's ever brought it up to the counter to query the price, let alone actually buy the bloody thing. We class that kind of album as obscure.'

I, of course, didn't have £13.99, so had to take the long slow walk of shame back to the front of the store, where I replaced the CD in its rack. I walked out of the shop, grumbling to myself about 'capitalist bastards killing music' and as I wasn't looking where I was going, didn't notice Jo walking towards me until I almost bumped straight into her.

A simple "watcha" was exchanged, no hug or kisses to both the cheeks as we weren't French. As always when I met Jo up town I knew that it was going to cost me money, in the form of "going for a coffee". It was the height of Peterborian sophistication to go for a coffee at a coffee shop, not a café. We had such a shop at the top of the Queensgate shopping centre that was glass fronted so that you could look down at the shoppers below.

Thanks to my carefully managed financial resource and my constant harping on about it, Jo knew with absolute certainty that she would be buying her own coffee. She had recently managed to get a Saturday job at the local Barrett's shoe shop earning £3 an hour so, compared to me, she was loaded. Whilst stood there saying "Watcha", I'd remembered that I only had £9 and a return bus ticket in my pocket, and still had to find a record shop that would sell me a Billy Bragg CD album at the correct price of £7.99. Quite simply I couldn't afford to go for a coffee, or even take the risk that I may have to pay for my own drink if Jo didn't offer to pay for us both. It didn't occur to me at any point to put off the buying of an album for a week and go for a coffee with my girlfriend.

I could feel a sense of terror at being denied the ultimate prize of a Billy Bragg album, so blurted out;

"I can't come for a coffee, I'm in a rush and I only have enough money to buy a CD. I'll see you at school on Monday, yeah."

I strode off, away from the girl who'd just wanted to spend half an hour of her lunch-break with her boyfriend. I had put a Billy Bragg CD before love. She should have saved herself a lot of heartbreak and grief and "packed me in" there and then. Instead she watched me wander off towards House On The Borderland. I'm not sure if she did watch me go. I didn't turn around. I was in a rush to get my hands on some Billy Bragg.

House On The Borderland was in a grim area of the city centre, squeezed between a late night burger bar and a tattoo parlour. It was run by an old hippy who would happily have banned all non-hippy types from entering.

The shop itself was stacked with thousands of vinyl albums and other 1970's memorabilia, with the scent combination of joss sticks, cats and damp clinging to my clothes and nostrils with such force that I wondered if the shops very existence depended on infecting unsuspecting customers with the smell. Whenever I walked in, I would look around and be convinced that the hippy wasn't actually on the shop-floor. Then…slowly…. he would rise from behind the racks of old Hawkwind records, looking like Dylan from the Magic Roundabout, and nod in my direction. It wasn't a nod of hello; it was a nod of "Hmmm that bloody boy is back in here again, seeing how many crap CD's and tapes he can get for a fiver".

A year later, Jo would fall head over heels in love with this shop and the whole new wave of crap hippy bands (Ozric Tentacles and the like) that rolled around in the early 90's preaching a need for tie-dye tops, braids and acid in order to "find yourself". But right then, I knew it was a shop that she wouldn't be seen dead in. Purposefully going into a place that I knew my girlfriend would never enter didn't seem like an odd thing to do, my mind was focussed on the prize. With the hippy's gaze burning a hole into the back of my head, I slowly approached the small CD section. It was well known that the old hippy felt that the only true way to listen to recorded music was on a scratched, warped 12" slab of vinyl recorded in Mono. But as I didn't get into music until 1990, I just wasn't used to buying vinyl regularly.

The only record player in our house was very clearly owned and operated by my dad. He didn't play much music in the house but, when Mum had gone out to an Avon party or to her Keep-Fit class, he would occasionally shout upstairs "I'm putting some good music on if you want to come down and listen, Jay?" In practice what this meant was him playing "Dark Side of the Moon" so loudly that all the windows in the house would rattle.

I would often seek refuge in the shed at such times of attempted musical education but he would always make me come into the house for what he saw as a musical education. I would listen to the racket for 30 seconds, scrunch up my nose and tell him "The words don't make any sense", at which point he would shut the front room door in disgust and I would escape upstairs. I was part of the CD generation. The first stereo that Mum and Dad bought me from Tandy's didn't even have a turntable for vinyl, just a CD and tape deck. As I'd already seen a Billy Bragg tape destroyed by over-playing I wasn't going down that route again, this purchase had to be a CD album.

The CD's in HOTB weren't in racks; they were just piled up in swaying towers on the floor in no particular order. Your first task when looking through them was to avoid knocking the tower over and thus incurring the wrath of the Hippy.

I was sure that he wouldn't have a Billy Bragg album amongst the Status Quo, Dire Straits and Michael Jackson CD's but, as every good 2nd hand music buyer knows, you have to look through every single pile/rack of CD's in a shop just in case you find a gem. That day I got very lucky. That day I found an album that was to quickly become a three times a day musical companion. That day, I found Billy Bragg's "Workers Playtime" for only 2 quid.

"Workers Playtime" is, in many ways, Billy's most personal album. It was written during the break up of an intense relation-ship and his thoughts and feelings are at times all too openly depicted in the songs. It had the social and political tracks that I was desperate to mainline into my brain, with the old soldier ballad of "Tender Comrade" and the life of the remand prisoner, as depicted in "Rotting On Remand". It also had the Braggist political manifesto set to music in the form of the life affirming

"Waiting For The Great Leap Forwards", which was a song I'd decided by the 3rd listen would be played at my funeral.

I skived off school the following Monday in order to continue my love affair with this amazing album, sneaking home after Mum and Dad had gone to work. It was the love songs on that album that had grabbed me. I had been having the occasional moments of emotional clarity where I realised that I was a crap boyfriend, so tracks like 'The Short Answer' found a welcome home inside my chest. It was as I was howling along in my room to that song that I realised that someone was throwing stones at the window. I pulled open the curtains to see Jo preparing another handful of grenades, so quickly opened the window.

Me - 'What the hell are you doing?'

Jo - 'Oh finally! I've been banging on the front door for the last 10 minutes. You do realise that you can hear that music halfway down the street don't you?'

Me - 'Alright Mum, give it a rest.'

Jo - 'When you didn't come into school, I wondered if you were ill or skiving, and now I know. So rather than come in and sit with me in French and have our usual Monday night date you decide to sit at home and listen to... What is it anyway?

Me - 'It's Billy Bragg and it's amazing. Come round the back, the door's open'.

Fortunately Jo also fell under the spell of "Workers Playtime". It became the album that we would listen to together whenever we had the chance. It was also the album that was the soundtrack to me taking the first faltering steps towards manhood in Jo's bedroom later that week. Jo was there as well, I should add. I had read in magazines that people set the mood for these fumbled sexual encounters with songs such as Marvin Gaye's "Let's Get It On" but our momentous occasion was soundtracked by Billy Bragg's "She's Got a New Spell", a tune that lasted an impressive 3 minutes and 26 seconds.

Jo and I were discovering life together and were having fun. I was though, unintentionally developing a masochistic edge when it came to music and our relationship. When we were having one of our happy periods, I would sometimes use 'Workers Playtime' as a blueprint to romance, decide that I was too comfortable and bring a little sabotage into our lives. This would take the form of little annoying things like not ringing her or ignoring her at school, just so songs like "Little Timebomb" and "The Price I Pay" would mean more to me when sat under my desk listening in the dark.

'Workers Playtime' introduced me to the extra special gift that was the duet. I had been a fan of the man/woman sing-along thanks to my exposure to Deacon Blue, but this was a different way of putting across lyrics and emotions. In the form of "Must I Paint You a Picture", "Workers Playtime" had a sublime duet. In the song, Cara Tivey and Billy dissect their relationship and their inability to understand each other's feelings. Jo and I would sit on the end of her bed, me resplendent in my new "Commercialism Is Killing Music" t-shirt (I didn't have a bloody clue what that slogan meant), and would sing the girl/boy words of the song back to each other. Sometimes it would be sung with smiles on our faces, full of adolescent spirit; at others it would be used as a way of letting the other know that they were bloody annoying without having to formulate our own words. My love for Billy Bragg had forced its way into every area of my life.

1991

Scratch My Name On Your Arm...

PEER pressure was all consuming at our school, a suburban secondary, the name of which could strike fear into other kids in the city. In early 1991, a self-mutilation craze spread amongst the pupils, which involved carving your girl/boyfriend's initials into your arm with the point of a compass. Later that year, Richie Edwards from the Manic Street Preachers would carve "4 REAL" into his arm in an attempt to horrify and impress Steve Lamacq. If he'd been a pupil at our school, Richie would most likely have been covered in teenage girls' initials.

I'm not sure if it was peer pressure or love for me that did it but, one cold February morning, Jo came bounding up to me in the corridor and proudly showed me her bloodied arm. There, scrawled into the skin of her left forearm, were my initials. At this point, I should probably have made a public show of saying "Wow, that's amazing" or a simple, functional "Thanks". Instead the conversation went like this:

Me: 'That looks painful.'

Jo: 'It really stings, but I wanted to have your initials on my arm, to show you how I feel about you.'

Me: 'Errrrr.....ok....'

Jo: 'Anyway I heard from Lisa that you'd carved my initials on your arm during Maths yesterday.'

Me: 'Errrrr.....not exactly.....'

Jo: 'What? You didn't carve anything onto your arm?'

Me: 'Errrr... No, well I mean yes I did, but....'

Jo: 'JAY.... (her shouting grabs the attention of our classmates, who are waiting in the corridor for their Humanities lesson to start)... what HAVE you got carved into your arm?'

With a proud smile, I pulled up my shirt sleeve to reveal my carving, and on my forearm proudly sat the bloodied initials:

BB

I looked from my arm up to Jo's face and my smile quickly faded. She didn't say anything, she didn't need to. She just burst into tears and ran off down the corridor, leaving me surrounded by my class-mates. One of the girls present decided to break the silence by simply saying; 'Wanker'. I didn't bother to find out who'd said it; they had summed up the situation superbly.

Throughout 1991, Jo and I would split up every couple of months. She would get bored of me 'being miserable' and would launch into tear-streaked diatribes about being able to 'find someone much better' than me. Or I would pack her in because I wanted to spend more time with my Billy Bragg albums. Unlike many of our peers relationships though, we did have a lot in common. Whether that be football, music or our ever more occasional ability to make each other laugh. After 2 or 3 weeks of being split up and having both vowed that this was 'the end for us', a conversation along these lines would take place in a corner of the school playground:

Me: 'Look, shall we just get back together or what?'

Jo: 'Ok, but things will need to change Jay. You need to be happier about life for one. I'm 16 now, I want to do exciting things, not just sit in your room listening to Billy Bragg or going for a fumble in the evenings behind the Science block.'

Me: 'Oh I'm sorry, I thought you enjoyed those things, my mistake. Christ, I tell you what, don't bother going back out with me. Go and find someone that is far more fun and can do these 'exciting things' you're after. No, actually let's get back together because being a mature 16 to my childlike 15, you can teach me how to be a grown-up.'

Jo: 'You really are a dick sometimes.'

Me: 'Tell me something I don't know....'

Jo: 'Fine, I can't be bothered to discuss it anymore, let's just get back together. Meet you behind the Science block tonight?'

Me: Sure, see you there at the normal time.'

I went back to listening to The Mock Turtles 'Can You Dig It?' on my Walkman and she went back to her gaggle of mates, no doubt to tell them how I had begged her to go back out with me.

The best night of our relationship was undoubtedly 29th December 1991. On that cold, post-Christmas night, as kids who were growing up too quickly, we went to a Billy Bragg gig at the legendary Hackney Empire in London.

Our local Way Ahead Box Office, was running a ticket and travel package from Peterborough. Many months before the gig, Jo and I had agreed that we should buy the tickets as Christmas presents to each other. She had wanted a 2nd hand Nintendo Gameboy as a gift, so had a deflated air of desperation and defeat in her voice when I finally got her to agree to go to the gig instead.

Come the morning of the 29th, I was bouncing off the walls of our house with excitement and changed my gig clothes at least 5 times before I set off to the coach pick-up point. I settled on black DM boots, black jeans and my black SexYOUality t-shirt. As I left the house, Dad asked if I was "Going to see Johnny Cash, dressed like that?" As always, when faced with one of his questions that I presumed was meant to be funny but didn't understand, I just said 'What?' and quickly wandered off before he could explain further.

I was convinced that the good people of Peterborough would be chomping at the bit to sit on a coach for 3 hours each way and head to east London to see Billy play. When I arrived at the designated meeting point, I was expecting to see a gleaming 52 seater coach and hordes of expectant fans. Instead, I was greeted by a clapped-out 16 seater mini bus and nobody else but the driver in attendance.

Jo turned up 15 minutes later, mildly annoyed that I hadn't been sat on my usual seat on the bus into town. The bus from her house had passed my stop, so we could have, in theory, arrived at the meeting point together. I had been far too excited to wait though so had caught the earlier bus. Where Jo found that 'weird' it seemed entirely reasonable to me. She was clad all in black, proudly displaying her 'Faith No More' t-shirt despite the freezing cold day.

Me: 'Oh.....'

Jo: 'Well that's a lovely hello isn't it! What's wrong with you now?'

Me: 'No, nothing, it's not important.'

Jo: 'Jay, I'm not spending the day with you having a face like that. What is it?'

Me: 'It's just; I thought you'd wear the Billy Bragg t-shirt that I got you for your birthday?'

Jo: 'Well I thought we would look a bit sad both wearing Billy Bragg t-shirts. Plus you know that Faith No More are my favourite band now.'

I waited until she had turned to get onto the bus, shook my head and got on board.

Eventually a handful of other gig-goers turned up and they piled onto the mini-bus. As we settled into the journey and watched the joys of the A1 roll by, I had 'that feeling', the one you get when you know beyond all doubt that you are going to have a special night. By this time, Jo had started to find my Billy Bragg obsession annoying and had worked out my "sabotage our relationship to make the lyrics more meaningful" stance. However, powered by nothing more than Cherry 7 Up and Smiths Square Crisps, which were both staple elements of my diet, we buzzed our way through the journey to Hackney.

I had been to a few gigs before our trip to east London but Peterborough only had two venues of note: A large hotel which had hosted the likes of Chris Rea and an over-sized YMCA Centre called The Cresset which had recently featured The Soup Dragons. Hackney Empire was quite different to either of those suburban halls. It was an atmospheric theatre that wore its working class roots proudly on its sleeve. We had seats in the upper circle but, like the rest of the crowd, spent the 90 minutes of Billy's performance stood up, swaying and singing along. He was on top form that night, playing lots of old favourites and songs from his recent album "Don't Try This At Home". It was a party atmosphere and we were totally caught up in it. I was desperate to soak up every second, every jagged rattle of the guitar and every word he sang had to be committed to memory. We didn't do anything crazily romantic like holding hands but, looking at Jo that night, I felt happy to be there with her, howling along to a man who had made a big impact on our lives. We left the theatre arm in arm, drenched in sweat from dancing, still singing the words to 'Accident Waiting To Happen'.

We should have had a quiet chat on the journey home and maturely concluded that the gig had been the high point of our relationship, that it would all be downhill from here, that we should just be friends from now on and get on with living our young lives. Of course we didn't do anything like that. We gazed in fearful wonder at the mean streets of east London, before falling asleep and dreaming of Billy Bragg. Soon we would be blundering blindly into 1992.

Not The Specs' Again . . . Please

AS 1991 drew to a close I was a fully fledged music and football fixated adolescent. Despite these twin obsessions and having a girlfriend and a loving family, the most important people in my life were my mates. Doody, Jacko, Mark, Shin and I had become a gang of lads that did almost everything together. Whether it was going to the football, sitting in Doody's bedroom listening to music or finding city centre pubs that would serve us alcohol despite us all being underage, we were all in it together. I knew that they were the only mates that I would ever need.

Through the 2nd half of the year, the boys and I had embraced a new wave of indie bands with loud, jangly guitars and often shouted vocals that were loosely tied together under the term "fraggle". Not that fraggle was a phrase that anyone outside of the offices of the NME ever used. The big 3 bands that we got into from that scene were Carter USM, Ned's Atomic Dustbin and Mega City Four. Musically they all sounded vaguely similar, and visually they had what was almost a uniform of long hair, long-sleeved band t-shirts, baggy shorts and DM boots (black or cherry red). Like all good teenagers we were desperate to copy our heroes dress sense. We didn't care that to any non-indie folks we looked bloody stupid. Like any youth trend worthy of the term, it was one that my parents absolutely despised. The fact that I was letting my hair grow down to my shoulders was of particular concern. To stop Mum from constantly moaning at me, we reached an uneasy truce which involved me keeping my long hair but on the understanding that I washed it every day. My hair, washed and conditioned looked more like a model's than the hairy arsed indie rock gods that I was trying to emulate. Mum would periodically try to smarten me up by buying me new clothes, but eventually gave up when she got me a Levi denim jacket and I promptly wrote "MEGA CITY FOUR" across the back of it in black marker pen.

It was a male dominated scene in terms of the bands and their fans. Ned's were 5 long haired lads from the West Midlands, whilst Carter were two shouty blokes with strange haircuts and cycling hats. Carter were the first band to introduce me to what seemed a magical but downtrodden land known as 'Sarf Landan'. Tales of Tulse Hill, Peckham and the lives of the folk that loved there instantly intrigued me and were another long drag on the political cigarette that Billy Bragg had lit and handed to me.

This wasn't a scene that Jo cared anything for. She would regularly agree with my mum that I looked, 'Stupid in those long Ned's shorts in the middle of winter'. She was getting ever more into the American rock, with her new friends, the likes of Faith No More and the Red Hot Chilli Peppers being her new loves, and that was music that I despised. We were becoming a couple held together by sticky tape and a mutual love for The Posh and Billy Bragg. By November, my hair was longer than hers, which she hated and got us some funny looks whenever we were out together.

In December, thanks to a miracle sent down by the indie gods, a kind promoter put on a Ned's gig at The Cresset. The boys and I all got tickets the day they went on sale by taking the day off school and getting 2 buses to be outside the venue when the ticket office opened at 9am. I thought that showed my dedication to the band. My girlfriend informed me in her developing New York/Peterborough accent that it was 'Lame'.

I rushed home from school on the day of the gig and dressed in my predetermined uniform of a Neds 'Godfodder' t-shirt, Carter USM shorts and my black DM's. As always, when we needed to go somewhere over the other side of town, I persuaded Dad to give us a lift. Six of us piled into his Vauxhall Cavalier and we sat on each other's laps for the 4 mile journey.

We got to the venue and it was as we watched the flood of people going through the doors that it dawned on me that as a nine stone weakling, wearing glasses, I was about to enter a darkened room surrounded by 800 people throwing their arms, legs and hair in all directions. I had read about Roman Gladiators in my school history books and now I knew exactly how they felt before going in with the lions.

Three weeks previously my beloved Peterborough United had played and somehow managed to beat, the then mighty Liverpool in the League Cup at our London Road ground. As the winning goal went in, the crowd around me went absolutely bonkers and, before I knew it, my legs were flailing desperately in the air above my head and I was tumbling down the concrete terracing. The euphoria of the goal kicked in and for a full 30 seconds I was a deliriously happy young man hugging total strangers. Then, as I picked myself up, I could feel the cut on my lip, a tooth that suddenly felt loose and spotted an odd jagged shape in my line of vision. I had broken my glasses.

As the rest of the city partied into the night to celebrate this famous victory, I had to go home and break the news about my specs to my mum. As I'd been wearing glasses since I was 3, Mum was well used to having to drag me along to Boots to get them replaced via an emergency appointment, but that never stopped her being absolutely fuming each time it happened.

That night, Mum gave me the "If you can't behave at football I will stop you from going" speech with added "If I find out that you are behaving like those hooligans we see on the TV, I will tell your dad." Two points to make here:

1. I actively ran away from any trouble that I saw at football matches. I'd never seen a football hooligan that wore glasses. Even if I'd wanted to be a hooligan, I would have been useless. One clip 'round the ear from an opposition fan and I would be scrambling around on the floor shouting, "STOP! Do you know how much these glasses cost???".

2. "I will tell your dad" was the ultimate threat in our house. It would occasionally be used by Mum to stop me and my sister playing up but the few times Dad did get "told" about my misdemeanours, upon his return from work, I would run to my room and barricade the door, not caring that I would miss my tea.

Back to the Neds gig and, as the band took to the stage, I looked around the pitch black hall and saw hordes of men in their late teens or early 20's, many with multiple face piercings and suspicious body odour, and wondered if we should go and stand near the back. Just as I was about to suggest this to my mates, the band kicked into their first song and the crowd surge that rolled from the back of the room like a tidal wave picked me up like a ragdoll and flung me around whilst I watched my glasses fly off into the distance. I was falling, desperately grasping at thin air trying to save them from a certain crushing but to no avail. Soon enough, gravity took hold of my skinny 15 year old frame and I found myself dumped face down on the floor. I quickly realised that blood was flowing from my nose and just below my eye, thanks to the fact that one of the plastic nose-clips from my specs had managed to imbed itself into my skin, which was particularly painful.

As at the Posh v Liverpool match, here I was, in the middle of a delirious crowd scrambling around on the floor trying to find my specs. I shook my head clear of its mild concussion just in time to see a white bloke with long, dirty dreadlocks gleefully pick them up and hurl them into the darkness. As I saw them arch high over the crowd, I knew that another terrific night out had been ruined by my specs, and specifically my inability to keep them on my face. I did my best to enjoy the rest of the gig but I knew that the broken glasses argument wasn't far away.

When Dad picked us up, he decided to not mention the fact that for the first time in 12 years I wasn't wearing my glasses or that my nose was covered in blood, which was good of him. My Mum, on the other hand, went up the wall when I got home. Another week spent grounded was the penalty handed down by the High Court of Mum, with the judge refutting my mitigating circumstances and turning down my appeal.

1992

Goodbye to Faith No More

AS much as I was an avid fan of both Ned's and Carter USM, the band from that scene that I really took to heart was Mega City Four. They were an indie band with loud but jangly guitars, led by a singer called Wiz who wore his heart on his sleeve. Every one of their songs told a tale from the eternal disaster that seemed to be Wiz's love life.

Their album "Sebastopol Road" was the last LP that Jo and I listened to together for hours on end. The guitars were just about loud enough to satisfy her love of American rock music and the lyrics were something we could both relate to. For the first few months of 1992 it was rare to find us in one of our bedrooms not listening to it. In real life we were growing up and apart so being able to scream along to Wiz's tales of pain, deceit and breaking up seemed to us like a mirror being held up to our increasingly grim relationship. Jo had decided that she had been the passive partner in our relationship for too long and was determined to rival me in the pain in the arse stakes. She was now the one not bothering to phone or choosing to ignore me if the mood took her. Our teenage love affair was a mess.

In March, one of our older friends, Lee, moved into his own house and, for better or worse, it changed the course of our adolescence. By now we had evolved into a group of about a dozen lads and girls, all roughly the same age, hanging around together. Relationships could start and end in a single night amongst the group and it all seemed perfectly normal. Before Lee got his house, much of our hanging around took place between the hours of 6pm-9.30pm (10.30pm at the weekend) either inside the tiny kid's playhouse at the local rec with 2 cans of cider each, or in the clearing in the local woods. At Lee's we had a stereo, a fridge for the alcohol and a whole group of wannabe young adults wanting to have fun. Well, I say a whole group but, to be honest, I didn't find it fun being at Lee's. Ideally, I would have been put in charge of the stereo, selecting the tunes for my friends to listen to as they coupled off, but of course that was too much to ask for. At least half of the group, powered by cheap booze, wanted control of the stereo. In between the indie songs I selected we would have to listen to the Levellers or, worse still, Back to the Planet. I absolutely despised The Levellers and the "crusty" scene they had created, but most of the girls in our group loved them. In fact Jo was the only girl I knew that didn't fall for The Levellers' fiddle and fleas rubbish. I loved her for that. The problem for Jo's indie obsessed boyfriend was that she was falling ever deeper in love with the US rock scene. This also meant that she was spending more time with her new friends who were generally all older than us and could easily get her into pubs and Peterborough's only 'rock club'. She did try to include me and introduce me to her new gang but I wasn't interested. They liked music that I hated with a passion, and more importantly I already had my mates, I didn't need any new ones. She soon gave up.

I wanted to be this pained introspective indie type with long, lank hair. She wanted to dress and act like she was in a rock band. Where she used to write things like 'I love Jay' on her school bag, she now had a huge Faith No More sticker.

We split up and got back together more times than Oasis,

often following bitter rows played out at Lee's house in front of our friends on a Saturday night. After such rows/splits, I would usually manage to wrestle control of the stereo and put Mega City Four on whilst looking forlornly into the middle distance and sipping from a can of Carlsberg. Unlike during my Billy Bragg period, I hadn't purposefully sabotaged our relationship to make the song lyrics seem more meaningful, but on those nights it would feel like Wiz was singing those songs just for me. I was listening to tracks with titles like "Wasting My Breath" and "What's Up?", while Jo (quite understandably) sought comfort in the arms of others, often in the same room that I was in.

I was beginning to realise that teenagers had a unique ability to disregard the social norms that most adults follow. During the first 3 months of the year, with us splitting up and getting back together, Jo ended up snogging over 50% of my mates. I'm not judging her or being mean, it was just how things happened in our group back then. As a dalliance between two members of our group ended, another emerged to take its place. Most of the group could deal with these mini love affairs by simply pulling up their jeans and carrying on with the night. I would use these situations to what I thought was my advantage and quickly perfected my heartbroken scowl. With my Mega's long-sleeved t-shirt pulled over my hands, I would sit and wallow.

Eventually, realising that as Jo was in an upstairs room with one of my mates, we probably weren't going to get back together that night, I would leave Lee's to go home and listen to my Walkman until sleep took over. On Sunday mornings I would wake up, crack open a fresh 6 pack of TDK C90 cassettes and spend the day making compilation tapes. Most of those tapes were made for me, heartfelt songs to make me feel better or, more often, worse. The lyrics of the Mega's songs that filled the tapes weren't exactly subtle or poetic but they comforted my 15 year old hormones, as I liked to imagine they did for thousands of similar morose folk around the country. Some of the compilations were made exclusively for Jo. I wasn't emotionally capable of showing my caring, loving side in words or actions, but in the 14 or 15 tracks that you could fit on one side of C90 tape, I would use songs to express what I couldn't. I bet most of the time she threw them into the bin without even listening to them or looking at the carefully handwritten track listing and lovingly selected lyrics sheets that accompanied them.

By March, both Jo and I were sick of splitting up and getting back together on a fortnightly basis but couldn't quite give up on what we had. We didn't have a dramatic final break-up, it was more of a mutual agreement. It happened one night, as we sat in her bedroom listening to music:

Jo: 'Jay, are you happy?'

Me: (smiling) 'Not listening to Faith No More I'm bloody not, no.'

Jo: 'You know what I mean.'

Me: 'You mean, am I happy with our relationship coz you're not and want us to split up for good this time?'

Jo: 'Well?'

Me: 'Well, was I right about what you meant?'

Jo: 'Maybe.'

Me: 'I think it's really a yes or no answer don't you?'

Jo: (laughing) 'Yes you were right. Look can we agree to just split up for good and be friends?'

Me: (pulling on my coat) 'I would agree to anything to get out of this room and not have to listen to that rubbish. Ok, let's call it quits, see you tomorrow at school yeah?'

It was as simple and pain-free as that to end our 18 month exploration of our constantly evolving hormones.

With my relationship no longer taking up valuable time, I got to fully devote myself to indie music, my mates and The Posh .

Posh didn't stop winning from January 1992 until the end of that season in May; well at least it felt like that. Slowly but surely I could sense the space in my chest that Jo used to occupy being replaced by a ginger haired centre forward called Tony Adcock. He was a graceful striker with a sharp eye for goal and a touch that was pure class. As the season progressed, Posh had a genuine chance of promotion into a league that we had never competed in before. We were looking at potentially the greatest team that the club had ever produced. After a 2-2 draw at London Road in the play-off semi-final v Huddersfield Town, we travelled to their Leeds Road ground more in hope than expectation for the 2nd leg. Against all the odds, we managed to win 2-1, thanks to a fantastic diving header from Stevie Cooper. That win meant that for the first time in our history The Posh were off to Wembley, for the play-off final v Stockport County.

Our school wasn't normally a hot bed of Peterborough United fever, with just a few of us wearing our Posh scarves and shirts in amongst the hordes of Liverpool and Manchester United fans, but it was in the week leading up to Wembley.

My mates had all made their travel plans for the game by studying the train timetable and tube map. Unfortunately my mums fixation with "hooligans" took over my plans and, despite repeated pleas, tantrums, tears and threats to purposefully fail my GCSE's she refused to let me travel by train. I was getting desperate and decided to change tack and asked my dad to drive me to Wembley. He laughed heartily at that request, his reserves of enthusiasm for football still dry after that England v West Germany semi-final in 1990.

Running out of options, I had only one left, the official supporters club coach. I was gutted to have to join the "window lickers" as they were known. Even though a couple of lads I knew from school were on the same one as me, I still had a face like a slapped arse on the morning of the game. I got to the coach park at 10am to find my schoolmates drinking illicit cans of warm Special Brew. Always a partial sucker for peer pressure, I took a cursory swig of the thick treacle like brew and got on board.

My schoolmates quickly realised that as the coach steward had a "no alcohol, on pain of death" rule, between the 3 of them they had to drink 6 cans of Special Brew before they could get on board. At £1 a can they weren't going to throw them away.

I settled down in my seat and, thanks to my copy of "Catcher in the Rye" and a football themed compilation tape on my Walkman, the journey whistled by. Then, onto the horizon came the almost mythical sight of the twin towers of Wembley. As promised, my mates were waiting for me upon arrival and we excitedly bowled into the ground and took our seats. I could describe the match blow by blow but I won't. The summarised version is that we were winning 1-0 with 5 minutes to go, with everyone in our ranks stood on their seat, hollering for the ref to blow for full-time. Then our 'keeper made a mistake and in the blink of an eye Stockport had made it 1-1. I sank back down into my seat, head in hands, close to tears and whimpering about how unfair life was. I was consumed by a familiar sense of doom, that the day and the season were all falling apart in front of my eyes. We had got this far, all the way to Wembley, only to throw it away. I was already dreading the coach home, with some people no doubt saying bloody stupid things like "It's only a game". I was especially dreading getting home to my dad, a man who would take the mickey out of any situation that I found myself in, no matter how grim it was.

Thankfully it didn't quite pan out like that. Jacko pulled me to my feet and back to standing on my seat just as we came close to conceding another goal. As we stood there, waiting for the inevitable defeat, the Wembley clock ticked down to show only 2 minutes remaining. At that moment, the ball fell to our cultured midfielder, Marcus Ebdon, who looked up and played possibly the greatest pass of all time to our star striker, Kenny Charlery. Kenny got his legs moving for one last effort, controlled the ball and powered towards the Stockport goal. The next moment is locked in time as we all stood, open-mouthed in anticipation, as he shaped to shoot.

I can say without fear of over-exaggeration that Kenny's sublime shot hitting the back of the Stockport net was the best moment of my young life. The seething mass of 25,000 Posh fans stood behind the goal, exploded. In yet another tumble of arms and legs (I later counted that I fell down six rows of concrete steps), we were all as one – in a scene that looked as if all of us had been wired to the mains electricity for 30 seconds.

The aftermath of the goal saw grown men hugging complete strangers and openly crying with joy. A blackmailer could have made a fortune with a camera that day, as many of those fellas wouldn't have wanted anyone outside the stadium to see them in such an emotional state. I could have died there and then a deliriously happy young man, screaming and crying with joy into the faces of my best mates. It was a moment that none of us would ever forget.

As a group of teenage lads we were never shy of a hug. We were the antithesis of our fathers who were far too tough and working class to ever spontaneously embrace another man. But as the final whistle blew it was hugs, kisses and sheer unbridled joy as far as the eye could see. We stood in the most wonderful Peterborough United themed glow and vowed to always remember that day, to always support The Posh. Standing on my seat, tears of joy rolling down my cheeks, watching our captain, the inspirational Mick Halsall, pick up the play-off winner's trophy, I looked around the ground at the thousands of Posh fans and drank in every last moment.

Ten minutes later we danced our way out of Wembley

and embarked on a wacky-races style chase to get back to Peterborough's Cathedral Square, in order for the party to start. As we came back up the A1, with about 20 miles still to go, at every bridge crossing the motorway were people waving blue and white Posh scarves, cheering and clapping the buses and cars home. It was a surreal and humbling sight, like we were victorious warriors being welcomed back to our home village.

Skipping merrily along the city centre streets (I was actually skipping), I looked across the road and there, in front of Woolworths, stood Jo. Being in a buoyant mood for once, I felt compelled I had to go over and speak to her even though she was with her dad who, understandably, had never been my biggest fan. We had shared so many of the high and lows of the last few Posh seasons; I knew we had to share this one. It was only as I skipped the 50 yards across the street that it dawned on me that she might not be pleased to see me. Luckily she greeted me with a smile, a yelp of delight (I assumed that was because of Posh winning, rather than seeing me) and a hug. We stood and talked for 10 minutes about the game before moving on to the inevitable "So how are you doing anyway?" conversation. Thankfully her dad had moved up the street by this point. Enthused by a combination of the joy of Posh's win, our affection towards each other and let's be honest here, habit, we talked about getting back together. We spoke of changing things, of doing more fun stuff but deep down we both knew that it was over and should stay that way. We stood there and said our farewells as a city went absolutely bonkers all around us. A quick hug and she was gone, into the mass of people staging the biggest impromptu party Peterborough had ever seen.

I stood on my own for a minute, outside Andy's Records, taking in what a crazy old day it had been. Then, with another skip, an inane grin on my face and clutching my trusty cans of Carlsberg Export I went to join my mates and the celebrations.

Well, first of all, I found a quiet phonebox and told my mum that I'd be late home.

It was one helluva party in Cathedral Square, crowned by our victorious manager and captain turning up to show the trophy to the delirious fans. They were promptly mobbed. I was just happy that I had finally had a good night out and not broken my glasses.

Reading, Writing & Tim Burgess

WITH the football season over, thoughts turned to the summer and what we would do to celebrate/commiserate our GCSE results. Our little group had talked a lot about going to our first music festival. As Glastonbury had already taken place, we had little option but to plump for the Reading Festival, which was set to for the August Bank Holiday weekend.

The excited chatter was of going to the festival and undertaking the classic British rite of passage into adulthood, namely: drinking, standing in a field listening to live music and sleeping in a leaky tent, hopefully with a member of the opposite sex. I joined in heartily, not least because Mega City Four were scheduled to play a Friday afternoon set. The reality was that I had a growing sense of certainty that Mum wouldn't let me go. I knew that she would point out that I was only due to turn 16 three weeks before the festival and that I was too young to go. When I told Mark about my concern he simply said "You'll be 16 by then, you can do what you want!" Ah yes, the 16th birthday landmark that we all looked forward to, knowing that once we had reached it we had the key to total freedom. Suffice to say, it didn't quite work out that way for any of us. The day after that landmark birthday, I was still doing the washing up and looking after my kid sister during the school holidays whilst my mum and dad went to work. It's pretty hard to rebel on a diet of sex, drugs and rock 'n' roll when you are looking after your kid sister for 8 hours a day.

In early July we had reached decision time, and I had to talk to Mum about whether I could go to Reading. Everyone else had already obtained their parents' permission, and a group of intrepid, youthful adventurers was forming. Unfortunately, I just couldn't see any way that Mum was going to let me go. Six weeks prior to this she hadn't let me travel to Wembley for the football via train as it was "too dangerous". Now I was all set to ask her to let me go away for 4 nights to sleep in a field, drink beer, watch bands and potentially share tent space with girls. I decided to sit her down one night after tea to discuss this thorny issue.

I made a big deal of sitting Mum down at our dining table. I didn't bother involving Dad as I knew that he would just defer to Mum anyway. We all knew and accepted where the balance of power was in our house. I was a jangling bag of nerves as I stood up (for extra gravitas) and blurted out, 'Can I please go to Reading Festival please? Doody, Jacko, Mark and all the others are going and it will be brilliant and I will be sensible as always, and there are loads of bands I want to see and you can trust me because I am too boring to do anything bad. It's for 4 nights and we will stay in a tent and it will be a top birthday present and to celebrate my GCSE's finishing and I won't drink too much and will walk into town every day to phone you.'

I stood panting, knackered from the exertion of getting all that out in one breath, and waited. After only a moment's hesitation she said:

"If you take the coach there and back, rather than the train, then you can go."

I stood catching flies, the shock kicking in, and was rendered temporarily speechless. I eventually recovered my senses, gave her a huge bear hug and a 'Thanks Mum, you won't regret this I promise.' I had a feeling that my looking nervous and worried swung it. I think she was so relieved not to hear that I had got someone pregnant or started taking heroin that she was happy to agree to almost anything. I dimly recall her saying that, as Doody was virtually an adult (he would turn 18 in October), that she was sure that he would be sensible and keep us all in line. Thankfully Mum had only met Doody a handful of times, and his Irish heritage meant that he already had a Master's Degree in charming relatives from the University of Life.

The Wayahead Box Office once again provided us with the ticket and travel package for the festival. I had to get a sub from my Nan to find the £80 needed, and then thoughts turned to tents. None of our group owned one so we decided to hire one for the weekend. Mark's mum drove us over to the tent hire shop and we stood there listening to the "tent man" giving us his marketing spiel. I quickly realised I had made a mistake in not bringing my dad along. Dad knew about everything practical in the world and would have known exactly what we needed. Tent man realised that an easy kill was available and somehow managed to persuade us that we needed a huge 6-man tent that didn't have a fully waterproof fly-sheet. As he stood lustily counting our hard-earned cash, he offered us a shark like smile and assured us that the tent was "showerproof".

As the excitement around the festival began to take hold, I would get photocopies of the line-up and make lists of all the bands that I wanted to see. For some people, festivals are all about drink, drugs and copping off. For me, those things were all minor interests compared to the music. Packing for your first festival is not an easy task. I'm sure arctic explorers take less food and toiletries than my mum insisted on stuffing into my rucksack. As well as the "essentials", I also had to make sure I had enough room for at least 2 band t-shirts per day. I had to look the part.

It was only a few days before we due to depart for Reading that we realised our coach was due to leave Peterborough at 10am. The problem with this was that our GCSE results were to be made available for collection from our school on the same day but not until 10.30am. This caused some mild panic amongst our travelling party. Personally, it worked out exceptionally well. My mum was delighted that she would be the first person to see my results by going to collect them on my behalf. Other kids in the same situation may have made their mums promise not to open the envelope until they could locate a telephone box and call home. I knew it was an absolute waste of time even mentioning such a scenario to mine. No matter what anyone said, she was going to be the one opening that envelope. My thinking was that this was one of those rare 'win-win' situations. I got to attend my first music festival and Mum got to be the first person to find out whether I had an academic future.

I didn't sleep very much the night before we left. I wasn't worried about my GCSE results; I was concerned about whether I would get to see all the bands that I was desperate to see over the course of the weekend.

I was up and about early on the morning of travel and got the standard pep talks from my parents:

Dad – 'Be careful' – simple, efficient and broad enough that if I did anything wrong he could be annoyed with me upon my return.

Mum - 'Don't let me down and don't do anything that will show me up, Jay.' The use of my name provided the desired extra menace. In my wired, excited state I wasn't sure if she was talking about the festival or my impending GCSE results.

As our gaggle of hormonally charged teenagers boarded the coach, I paid only fleeting notice to the fact that it was raining. I had taken my coat out of my rucksack to make room for that week's edition of the NME and my emergency Carter USM t-shirt. Not to worry, I'd thought, it's August bank holiday weekend, I won't need a coat.

The journey consisted of eating all of our lovingly made

packed lunches and sipping on illicit cans of Special Brew that Doody had sneaked aboard. Upon reaching Reading we were dropped off at the entrance to the site. After we had politely queued to exchange our tickets for the festival wristband, we entered the campsite and it struck me how normal the place looked. It was simply a scattered array of tents, some portaloos and the kind of burger van that it was always wise to avoid in Peterborough city centre on a Saturday night if you wanted to get out of the bathroom on the Sunday. I couldn't see my life changing here.

While we finished the last dregs of the, now warm, Special Brew, we put up our marquee style tent whilst arguing over groundsheets, flysheets and guy ropes. Once our weekend accommodation was complete, we decided to take a walk into the town centre to stock up on vital alcohol supplies. This meant dragging 24 cans of Hofmeister each back from Reading town centre. That mile-long journey was unbridled agony. I don't know about "follow the bear", I reckon the bastard had been sat on my back during that particular ordeal.

Mark and Jacko used the cover of the long slog back to the festival site to find a phone box to call their respective mums and discover their GCSE results. I didn't. It wasn't that I wasn't interested in my results, it was more that I wanted one night at the festival enjoying myself in blissful ignorance, before calling home and getting the potentially bad news. Mark and Jacko knew that they were going to get good results; they were both intelligent lads who had worked hard. I was more a middle of the class student. I'd always done reasonably well, not due to any natural intelligence but thanks to a love of reading, the ability to retain a few salient facts and the gift of waffling.

Doody had taken his GCSE's the previous year and was working in a local factory. We were all envious of him having "cash on the hip" and not having to count his loose change to see if he could afford another pint of lager or portion of chips. Fair play to Doods though, he was always generous and was never shy in buying me and Jacko a pint when we were invariably skint.

The sun was starting to set as we returned to the campsite and recovered from our lager march. The sun going down seemed to ignite something in this small corner of Berkshire. Campfires were lit, cans were opened and a lingering, pungent smoke filled the air and clung to my nostrils. For the first time in my life, I heard a wolf howl. It took me a full five seconds to realise that wolves didn't inhabit Reading.

Watching my first festival come to life, I was a gibbering muddle of excitement and apprehension. I saw people with piercings and hairstyles that I'd never imagined were possible, let alone seen on the streets of Peterborough. As these older teenage miscreants and fully fledged adults began their rapid descent into the Village of the Damned, we sat and quietly sipped our lager and ate our Mini-Cheddars. Slowly but surely the alcohol kicked in and we finally felt brave enough to put some music on the ghetto blaster that we had brought along and had ourselves a little party. We had recently discovered a sparkling wine called "Pink Lady", which tasted foul but was cheap and, most importantly, the pressure inside the bottle was so strong that the cork could be fired over the top of a house when popped. We'd carried out scientific experiments on Doody's estate to produce such findings. At Reading, like the children we were, we stood in the campsite and cheered as the cork flew from our bottle and over the sea of tents. We glugged down the sweet, sticky contents and lost another layer of our inhibitions.

We must have resembled a group of young antelope as the festival lions picked up our scent and began to hungrily visit our encampment. As night descended, we were offered everything from beer at £4 a can, hash, trips and pills that I was pretty sure my mum took for backache. I'd thought that I was pretty streetwise when it came to drugs as, like every other kid in the UK, I had watched enthralled as Zammo got hooked on heroin in Grange Hill. But, up until that night, I hadn't ever been in a situation in which I had to "just say no". As darkness began to descend, a crusty type in a Levellers t-shirt and the worst dreadlocks I'd ever seen sat down in our camp to educate us wannabe rebels about the joys of hash. I wasn't bothered about getting involved but peer pressure and the fear of ridicule saw me taking my place in the eagerly formed circle as a spliff, that was the size of the Camberwell Carrot, was handed around. I sat there secretly dreading the moment that it would be my turn for a toke. I suddenly felt like the squarest kid in the world as I'd never even smoked a full cigarette. It looked easy enough though. All you had to do was suck as hard as you could on the end of the spliff and take as much smoke as possible down into your lungs before casually letting it drift out of your mouth. I'd always looked up to Doody and would turn to his 17 year old wisdom when I was having a crisis of confidence. He could see the apprehension scrawled across my face and said simply "It will be ok mate".

As the spliff came to Doods he took a long drag and then a couple of seconds later calmly blew a plume of smoke out of his mouth. He looked at me with a mixture of hope and pity, then passed it to me. As if sensing my fear, the weasel-faced crusty, piped up, 'Go on Joe 90, you'll enjoy that hash, man.' Joe 90, Jamie & The Magic Specs, and the simple "Four Eyed Twat", I'd been called them all over the years but, coming from the wannabe hippy it prodded my anger gene into action and I replied with a blunt; 'Piss off knobhead.'

He made an exaggerated show of being offended, by holding his hand to his mouth and cackling; 'Hark at Joe, looks like you need that spliff more than any of us, you need to chill out, man'.

A combination of murderous thoughts, a desire not to look a prat in front of my mates, coupled with an inability to smoke, meant that I knew this wasn't going to end well.

With the red mist descending, I placed the spliff gingerly between my lips and took the longest pull my chest could manage. I had a glorious second of thinking, "wow, got away with that, I feel fine", before the burning sensation hit the back of my virgin throat and my chest reacted by doing everything it could to expel the poison from my body as quickly as possible. The smoke flew back out of my mouth and left me wracked with body-convulsing coughs. I could hear the laughs from the hippy and some of my so-called friends before I could even manage to open my eyes.

The utter humiliation was building with every cough and tear that rolled from my eyes and I became aware that I was now making enough of a scene to attract the attention of everyone within a 100 yard radius. Just as I thought the end was coming and that my cause of death would be recorded as "smoke inhalation and shame", Doody stepped forward and poured lager down my red-raw throat. I used this slip back into reality to grab my own can, my Walkman and stomp off into the distance. As I pulled my headphones on and the comforting bark of Billy Bragg filled my ears, I could still hear the bloody hippy laughing and shouting; 'That was magnificent Joe, come back and have some more.'

I set out to get away from our campsite and explore the festival as my coughing fit slowly died out. I would soon discover that being alone at festivals and getting lost in them was something that I greatly enjoyed but as a lad who had only left Peterborough for football matches and the odd gig to the non-bohemian towns of Northampton and Lincoln, the walk around the site that night was a real eye-opener.

Even though the festival didn't officially start until the following day, many of my fellow festival-goers had already imbibed their recommended yearly allowance of cider. This was truly the age of the crusties, and even Reading with its rock music reputation was seen as fair game for them to invade. Of course they didn't want to do anything as crazy as actually pay for a ticket to get in.

With "Workers Playtime" on my Walkman, I wandered the site and saw people passed out, face down in the mud. Others were stripped to their pants, dancing to some industrial rave track, while jugglers and fire-eaters seemed to be around every corner. I made my way round to the entrance to the main arena, only to discover, with a genuine leap in my chest, that the gates were open and anyone with a wristband could wander in. There is a strange mix of the urban and the countryside when a festival arena is devoid of people. I sat there for a couple of hours, propped up against the crash-barrier at the front of the main stage, drinking my beer and taking in my surroundings. Everyone has those special places where they can go and feel utterly relaxed, and I had found mine, sat in front of that stage in a deserted main arena. No music playing, people rushing around going about their business but not noticing me sitting there, was heaven. As it was August Bank Holiday weekend, my period of Zen-like calm was eventually disturbed by the rain starting to pour down.

Everyone was absolutely plastered by the time I got back to our campsite, with plenty of them supposedly feeling the effects of the spliff. As the heavens remained open, we took shelter in our tent, only to find that showerproof did not mean "able to cope with a biblical downpour". With soaking wet clothes and sleeping bags, we attempted to settle down for the night. A couple of minutes later, the girls tent fell to the ground under the weight of the rain and wind and suddenly, 10 of us were trying to sleep in our dripping excuse for a tent. As we shuffled around in the dark, we realised that none of us had thought to bring a torch, so had to scramble around by the light of a glow stick. Faced with such conditions we decided to crack open the emergency bottle of Pink Lady and have a party in the rapidly forming puddles that were invading the groundsheet.

Despite the storm rumbling above their heads my fellow campers all slept well, but I was up early on the Friday morning and eager to go for a wander. As I slopped through the primordial mud in my sodden Mega City 4 shorts and Billy Bragg t-shirt, I happened upon a large tent with 'The Samaritans' emblazoned on the front. A friendly woman in her mid 30's beckoned me inside and offered me the bargain of a lifetime; a cup of tea and 2 slices of toast for 40p. To an impoverished schoolboy, battered by the worst the weather had to offer, this was a sanctuary. I looked around the tent to see the only other guest being quietly and carefully talked down from a drug nightmare by one of the charitys volunteers. Thankfully I didn't need that kind of help from these lovely people but tea, toast and a dry bale of hay to sit on was a joyful relief from the elements. Every morning for the rest of the festival I would undertake the same routine of tea, toast and a chat while the rest of the campers snored their way through their collective hangover.

When I got back to the campsite, it was alive with talk about Sunday night's headliners, Nirvana. A band that were at the height of their powers but, due to Kurt Cobain's fragile mental and physical state, nobody was sure if they would appear at Reading that weekend.

We had a spare day-ticket for the Sunday, thanks to our mate Dave being caught with an Oxo-cube size lump of weed the previous week and thus being grounded by his mum. I stood outside the festival entrance for an hour trying to sell the ticket for its £25 face value, but to no avail. In the end, out of boredom and a desire not to waste anymore of my time, I sold it to a genial scouse ticket tout for a fiver. I then stood and watched in awe as he sold it to the lad stood next to him for £15. I hadn't seen touts first hand before and I was spellbound by the way he had made a tenner so easily.

Determined to throw ourselves head first into the festival, we filed into the arena with the hordes and cracked open our cans of cheap lager. We figured that, as we were at a festival, the "never drink before mid-day unless you want to become an alcoholic" rule that our parents had drummed into us could be relaxed.

The first band that I really wanted to see that day were Leatherface, a UK hardcore band who we had seen play in front of 20 people at a Peterborough club the previous month. As we wandered over to the Melody Maker tent to see their set, it became apparent that a lot more than 20 people were cramming themselves inside. Doody, even at 17, was a wise old head and said, "Why don't we stand near the back and get a decent view?"

I, of course, wanted to get to the front and throw myself into the mosh pit. My thinking was, I had been in the middle of the pit at Neds and Carter USM gigs, and they were bands playing to big crowds, this lot would be tame by comparison. I didn't want to take any chances though, so put my glasses into their hard backed case and stored them in the pocket of my army surplus combat shorts. I made my way to the front of the crowd just as Leatherface took to the stage. On the sound of the first chord being struck I knew that I had made a terrible mistake. As the people around me appeared to show no desire to listen to the music being played, I found myself spun around like I was in a washing machine, with the arms and legs of various people whirling around my head. I was now genuinely scared and, as the band banged out "I Want The Moon", I did my best not to get banged out by one of their fans. I somehow survived that first song with little more than an impending sense of doom and a string of spit hanging from the left shoulder of my Mega City 4 t-shirt. I knew my luck wouldn't hold for much longer.

As the next song kicked in, the violent aggression of the crowd cranked up another notch and I must have resembled a human yo-yo being thrown backwards and forwards. When the crowd surfing started, I knew instinctively that I had to get out of there, back to Doody and my can of Carlsberg. Initially I tried not to push or shove people out of the way but it was hard work and after about a minute of getting nowhere, I put my head down and marched through the mass of bodies. Then, only 50 yards away from safety, a big sweaty skinhead in a "Cockney Rejects" t-shirt, took offence to me making my way through the crowd and without saying a word, decided to smack me in the mouth. Thanks to the swaying motion of the packed crowd it was a glancing blow and, as the trickle of blood hit my tongue, I staggered away as he simply turned back to throwing himself around to the song as if nothing had happened. Finally I managed to reach Doody and flopped down next to him, covered in blood, sweat and beer. He looked at me, smiled smugly and said; "Busy down the front was it?"

I had survived my first, and last, UK hardcore mosh pit.

We walked from the Melody Maker tent to the main stage to see the band that meant it all to me, Mega City Four. It was my first time seeing them play live and I was bouncing up and down with excitement. As they ambled onto the stage in the late afternoon, I thought that this was my moment, this was my band. As they rattled through "Scared of Cats" and "Words That Say", I sang along to every word. For the first time in my life I experienced the therapeutic feeling of bounding around screaming along to songs in the open air. I didn't spend any time thinking about Jo but it was undoubtedly her that I was aiming those words at, despite her being 150 miles away. MC4 had been our band and, in the wilds of Berkshire, I finally moved on from our relationship. By the end of their set I was drenched in sweat and had an inane grin on my face. It was my moment.

How was I to know that less than 4 hours later I would find a band that would blow me away?

On Friday 29th August 1992, I found The Charlatans.

I knew of The Charlatans before that fateful night but had

written them off as just another Stone Roses clone band with one good tune in the form of "The Only One I Know". Doody was a fan though, so I'd agreed to stay and watch their set that evening to keep him company.

The drummer, bass player, guitarist and organist shuffled onto the cavernous main stage and began slowly building an atmospheric instrumental track. I was fast losing interest when the most beautiful man that I had ever seen lithely shimmied onto the stage. It was love at first sight. I had fallen for Tim Burgess, the lead singer of The Charlatans. I stood mesmerised, gazing at him as the opening song rattled the ground that we stood on and pushed the menacing storm clouds from the sky above us. I was pretty sure that I was straight but the feelings rumbling around my chest were of love, lust and desire. I applauded wildly along with the rest of the crowd as the band came to the end of that opening song, "You're Not Very Well".

Whilst reeling from my new found feelings for Mr Burgess, I was quickly introduced to one of the other elements that made this band extra special. Up on the stage, a man was hunched over a Hammond organ and hammering out a mesmeric riff. Rob Collins' inspired opening to "Weirdo" slid down my spine like electricity, forcing my legs to dance and my serotonin levels to reach a new found high.

I was in a sense of shock, totally gone, caught up in the moment, dancing like I was possessed to a song I didn't know, to a band that I didn't think I liked.

After a quick, "This is fucking amazing!" exclamation to Doody, I was back to dancing around the field to the likes of; 'Tremolo Song', 'Then' and 'Indian Rope'. Tim Burgess had the entire crowd in the palm of his hand with his incoherent between song ramblings being greeted with the same throaty cheer as a winning goal at Wembley.

That 50 minute Charlatans performance changed my

musical life. For the time that they were on stage, I didn't think about anything in the world other than the songs and Tim Burgess. I knew after a euphoric run-through of "The Only One I Know", about 20 minutes into the set, that this was my band and that they would become a massive part of my life. I looked over at Doody during that song and seeing his mad mop of curly hair bouncing around in delight, I knew that this was one of those moments, the type that sear into your brain and pick you up when times are crap with their unending pot of positivity. Dancing in a field, to the best live band on the planet, with my mate stood next to me, life couldn't get any better.

With only 9 minutes of The Charlatans allotted stage time left, things did get even better. Martin Blunt's heavily plucked slow bass rhythm was the start of the most amazing live song that I'd ever heard. The guitar and drums slowly came in before Rob Collins began to frantically smash away at the Hammond, then like an indie soothsayer, Tim wandered to the microphone and announced "This is where it all ends". I didn't know the words, I didn't know the tune, I didn't even know the name of the song but I danced as if my life depended on it. The majestic beauty of "Sproston Green" lit up the night and left me in a state of unbridled euphoria with an aching for more. As Tim departed with a final "Thank you very much indeed", Doody and I stood there giggling with delight before having a manhug, safe in the knowledge that we had just witnessed absolute genius.

The Wonderstuff headlined the main stage that night but I left them to it and sought out the bootleg tape stall that I'd read about in the pages of the NME. I was soon to discover that such stalls were dens of iniquity that sold illegal recordings of bands live sets minutes after they had left the stage. They were always poor quality recordings, on cheap tapes, with one colour (usually orange or bright green) paper inlay cards. Large groups of folks (usually eager young men with glasses) would crowd around the stall eagerly awaiting the delivery of a certain bands bootleg tape. That night, eventually the; "Charlatans from the main stage is ready" shout went up and I quickly handed over £5 to get my sweaty palms on the contraband tape.

It was only after buying my "The Charlatans – Roading (sic) 1992" tape that my adrenaline dropped to vaguely normal levels and it dawned on me that I still hadn't called home to find out my GCSE results. I wandered off site at 11pm to find a phone box without bothering to consider whether Mum would be asleep. She wasn't pleased to hear from me, especially as the phone in her bedroom was on Dad's side of the bed, so she had to reach over him to answer it. She was reasonably happy with my grades but then decided that, to be ringing her so late, I must be drunk. I assured her that I was having a lovely time and had only had our preagreed 3 pints a days before imitating the pips and insisting that I didn't have any more change. As I was putting the phone down, I could hear her growling; "Don't put the phone down Jay, I mean it….." I figured that I would deal with her mood when I got home.

As it was, I had enough GCSE's to go on to do my A-Levels and that was all I was bothered about. I had a festival to enjoy.

Saturday daytime was full of rain and crap bands. The evening though, featured my only contact with a female that weekend. I had never been good at talking to girls that I don't know but this was a particularly glorious failure. I had somehow managed to get split up from my mates during the early evening and ended up in the middle of the main stage field, which was fast turning into a swamp, as Ride took to the stage. Emboldened by my experience with The Charlatans, 24 hours previous, I thought I should give these shoegazing indie types a listen. They turned out to be another revelation – not in the Charlatans standard of earth shattering revelation, but a revelation to me nonetheless. Ride's set that night was mainly made up of tracks from their recently released "Going Blank Again" album. As they blazed their way through their set of multi-layered indie-pop, the heavens re-opened. Thousands of festival goers left the

Main Stage area to seek cover in the Melody Maker or beer tents. The dual vocal melody of the simian Mark Gardner and the ice-cool Andy Bell captivated those of us left in the sodden field. After a soaked to the skin jump around to the gorgeous "Twisterella", I realised two things:

1 – I was now stood in a gigantic puddle where, when I moved my feet, the water would gently lap over the top of my trusty DM boots and onto my freezing cold legs.

2 – A very pretty indie girl was dancing in the same puddle and she kept looking at me. By this time, due to the rain, my curtains hairstyle had been ruined and was pushed back to keep the wet hair out of my eyes. This wasn't the kind of look that anyone was going for and, coupled with my rain streaked glasses and black Carter USM top, I must have looked like a young, short-sighted Dracula impersonator.

No matter what the weather threw at us, me and the pretty girl with long dark hair and a "Curve" t-shirt, continued our puddle dancing. She kept looking over and I kept looking over, she kept looking over and I kept looking over (repeat to fade). At times we would be dancing in our new watery home, brush inadvertently against each other, and smile, but still neither of us said a word. I was desperate to say something, anything to her:

'Hi, do you often stand in a huge puddle watching bands?'

I didn't say a word despite her smiles, sly and not so sly, looks at me and the fact that she was dancing ever closer to me. Due to the biblical downpour, whenever one of us moved, the wave effect in the puddle would splash freezing cold water all over our legs. I looked down and saw that she was wearing Adidas Samba Classic trainers so her feet must have been absolutely soaked. Still we didn't leave the puddle. Still neither of us said a word.

As the band ended their set with an epic version of "Mouse

Trap", even the few thousand hardy souls that had stayed out in the elements ran for cover. Me and "Ride Girl", as she was now forever to be known in my head, remained in our puddle. Finally after what seemed like an hour, but in reality was probably no more than 5 minutes, she turned towards me. My nerves raced up and took a firm grip of my mouth as she said slowly and forlornly; "So....see you then....." and walked at a snail's pace away from the puddle that had been our home for the last hour. All I could manage was a muffled "Err, bye..." and a sense of annoyance that I knew would linger.

I went and got a beer, two in fact, I needed them. I checked that Ride Girl hadn't returned to the puddle and then promptly got my head expanded by that nights main stage headliners. Public Enemy smashed their way into my indie-boy skull with a set of hip-hop rhymes and beats that were from another planet to the one that I inhabited.

The Sunday morning brought more rumours about whether Nirvana would play that night. More worryingly, it brought more rain. I stood, drenched, in the main arena admonishing myself for the 10,000th time for not bringing a coat. How I didn't get pneumonia I will never know.

Sets by Teenage Fanclub and Nick Cave & The Bad Seeds made everyone smile (TFC) and want to call their mum in fear (Cave). Then, in the pitch black of the wet Reading night, a blonde-haired figure was brought onto the stage in a wheelchair, dressed in what looked like a surgical gown. As Grohl and Novoselic beat out the rhythm to "Breed", Cobain rose from the chair and proceeded to enthral the expectant crowd. Despite not being a Nirvana fan, I couldn't help but be impressed by their performance that night. Cobain wasn't a traditional frontman, but he had a voice that felt like a cricket ball smashing you in the teeth and a quiet but firm control of the apostles. We all knew, stood there in 3 inches of waterlogged grass and mud, that this performance would be an "I was there" moment.

What a sparkling weekend it had been. I had been to my first music festival and was instantly hungry for more. I had fallen in love with Tim Burgess and his band and got soaked to the skin for 4 days. It felt like being initiated into the world of festivals was our final step on the road to adulthood. If you could stay in a tent for a weekend, watch bands, drink and smoke a spliff, what more was there to learn about life?

In reality, Doody aside, our intrepid group were all back at school the week after Reading. The big difference that September was that we were heading into the 6th Form. This provided the dual joy of being able to wear our own clothes and being allowed to call our Business Studies teacher "Malc" rather than Mr Mason. The only other major change to 6th form life compared to school was that we got to sit around in our dedicated common room and play Tetris on the Gameboy for hours at a time. Jacko and I were joined by Mark as he had managed to escape his catholic secondary school to come to the wrong side of the tracks. Being a good looking charmer, coupled with his new to the school status, at least a quarter of the girls in the lower-6th quickly developed a crush on Mark. I had made a conscious decision to let my hormonally charged peers get on with their brief couplings. I had a diet of music and football to keep me occupied.

I spent the rest of the year running the 300 yards home from school and playing whichever indie singles and albums I had managed to buy, borrow or steal. All I wanted to do was be able to close the door to my room, crawl under the desk and listen to Billy Bragg, The Charlatans and any other indie music that I could find. Music had become an addiction, one that I needed to feed on an hourly basis, with even the 2 minute walk from one class to another being filled with a quick blast of The Stone Roses or New Order on my Walkman.

Jacko and I had managed to secure gainful employment at our school, which had been renamed "Stanground College" over the summer as it had started to host evening classes. Our job was to put out the trampolines and judo mats for those classes. It was tough, at times dangerous, physical work for two slightly-built 16 year olds but we needed the £2 per hour on offer in wages. In order to ensure the trampoline was properly sprung, one of us would have to hold down one end with all their weight, whilst the other hung like a bat on the unsprung section until, eventually their weight would pull it down.

I didn't become a monk for the rest of the year as there was the odd one night dalliance between Jo and I. We would occasionally get bored or lonely, reminisce and then let nature take it's course. Laid in her bed afterwards we would reach another mutual decision that this wasn't a good idea and that we were "definitely splitting up for good" this time.

1993

Moz & Me

AS 1993 broke, my obsession with The Charlatans continued to grow. I hadn't cut my hair since seeing them at Reading in an attempt to emulate Tim Burgess' flowing locks. Following the critical slating that their recent album, "Between 10th & 11th", had received, they appeared to be in decline but to my teenage senses they were a peerless band that were on the up. I would sit in the space under my desk and listen to their debut album "Some Friendly" and marvel at songs like "Then", "White Shirt" and the swirling, Hammond organ driven slab of genius that was "Sproston Green".

Doods and I had bonded further over our mutual love of the band, and would regularly scrawl "Tim Burgess Is God" on walls, t-shirts and anything else we could find. We were desperate to see them play live again and would scour the NME and Melody Maker every Wednesday morning for any gig announcements. Then, one bleak January morning, I saw in the NME an advert for our dream gig:

Day Tripper – The Charlatans & Ride at Brighton Centre (12th March 1993)

Frustratingly, as Doody was at work, I had to wait until that evening to give him this life-changing news. I was only allowed to ring him at work in an emergency. Although I knew he was going to be excited about this gig, I didn't think even I could justify classifying it as an emergency.

I was still only 16, unlike Doody who was now 18, so had to convince my mum to let me go to the gig. Fortunately, as I hadn't returned from Reading Festival with a mohican, a tattoo or a drug habit, she felt I could be trusted and agreed that I could go and thankfully didn't insist that I took the coach to Brighton. She even agreed to buy the gig and train tickets on her credit card and for us to pay her back in instalments.

None of the rest of our little gang had fallen under The Charlatans spell, so the path to Brighton Centre was one that Doody and I travelled alone. The day of the gig was the first bright and breezy spring day of the year, with thousands of indie-kids descending onto the seafront, all able to ditch their long-sleeved band t-shirts for the short sleeved versions (often of the same design). We couldn't afford to drink in the local pubs as our spare cash needed to be saved for the prized commemorative "Daytripper" t-shirt. Instead we bought a case of beer, a bottle opener and retired to our seafront B&B to prepare for the biggest gig of our young lives.

We bounded up to the Brighton Centre later that evening, high on life and Becks. Even before either band took to the stage, the DJ hyped up the indie disco atmosphere with some of the best tunes of the time (including Belly – "Feed The Tree" and Radiohead – "Anyone Can Play Guitar"). Ride were first up with a shimmering hour of indie rock and fringe shaking. The Charlatans followed and were in imperious form, with a bouncing Tim milking every drop of adulation from the crowd. As "Sproston Green" rattled the windows of the venue with its "Apocalypse Now" helicopter outtake, Doody and I stood there ruddy faced, knackered, beaming and had our now traditional hug. It had been another magical Charlatans performance, one that we would both treasure.

We went back to our B&B and sat drinking, recalling the gig in intricate detail before falling asleep, still fully clothed, on the double bed that we had been assigned.

On the train home the next morning we bumped into a clearly still twisted Bobby Gillespie. Being perky young lads still high from nothing more than the gig, we ignored his obvious "Pish off and leave me alone" stare and asked him to sign our commemorative Brighton postcard. He scribbled his name then politely asked us to sod off.

The weekend had been as close to perfect as it was possible to imagine and I was thirsty for more. I was like a sponge, desperately sucking up any new elements of culture that I could find. I was reading 3 books a week; from Irvine Welsh to Oscar Wilde and watching films like 1984 and The Ipcress File, but my real passion remained indie music.

At the Daytripper gig, when the DJ was whipping up the crowd, he played a song that I hadn't heard before, that got my hips wriggling in a way that I'd never felt the urge to do previously. As the opening guitar riff kicked in, a voice from a planet somewhere outside the known universe began to question me about what turned me on and something called animal nitrate. I had absolutely no idea what he was blathering on about but I had received the telltale shot of adrenaline that forced me to dance and I knew instinctively that I'd found another band.

I knew about Suede before that night in Brighton, and had even caught a bit of their set in the Melody Maker Tent at Reading the previous summer. I had dismissed them as the new darlings of the music press who were taking valuable column inches from the likes of The Charlatans and Ride. They were acolytes of The Smiths and Morrissey, and that was not a compliment. But after hearing "Animal Nitrate" at the Brighton Centre, I hoovered up every radio session, single and live recording I could get my hands on and eagerly awaited the release of their debut album on 29th March 1993. That album was the signal for the start of a movement that the music press christened "Britpop".

The country as I saw it, was ruled by the 3-headed monster that was grunge, manufactured chart pop and the crusty scene. Britpop was a wake up call, which served to show that outstanding guitar music was being made in the UK. This was my time and in Suede we finally had an indie band that could take "Oveeeeeeer" the UK. Their eponymous album went to the top of the album charts on its week of release.

"Suede" was packed full of passion, urban drama and twisted spirit. It concentrated on the unglamorous side of sex, the coldness, the regret, revenge and anger. I adored every track but the singles (So Young, Animal Nitrate, The Drowners, Metal Mickey) were the highlights and provided a vivid soundtrack to the springtime.

Suede were a band that dragged you into their world. The music, the look, the androgyny, the whole package. They were definitely the band that annoyed my dad most, with me upstairs squealing along to 'Metal Mickey', while he was downstairs trying to watch the 6 O'clock News. He would come running up the stairs to complain only to find me, shirt undone to the navel, gently whipping myself with a microphone lead, singing along. At least once he just turned around and shouted "I give up on you Jay, I really do."

Despite my Brett Andersonesque dancing, my real hero in the band was Bernard Butler. Up to that point I had only really cared about lead singers. In my eyes, guitarists were the same as drummers and bass players, important but never worthy of adulation. However, when it came to Suede, you would have to have been a cloth eared halfwit to not realise that the real talent within their ranks belonged to the guitar wielding Butler.

I wanted to be Bernard Butler. Obviously, I didn't do anything as crazy as learn to play the guitar. As I had been growing my hair, I had it cut in his long bob style, bought some charity shop shirts and worked on the look. I didn't get close to it really but it was enough for me to become a bedroom impersonator.

It was Suede's obvious obsession with The Smiths that persuaded me to put my music press inflamed prejudices aside and give Morrissey another chance. For two years, Mark and I had sat in his bedroom listening to music, routinely ridiculing his younger brother Anthony who was in the next room listening to Morrissey. I had fallen for the myth that Morrissey was just a miserable git who was obsessed with songs about being run over by buses and girlfriends in comas. The combination of Suede and finally listening to the tunes Anthony was playing saved me from a life of happiness and introduced me to the world of Morrissey.

On a warm June day, I decided to take the plunge and finally determine whether or not I liked this indie icons songs. I trundled into town on the bus and back to House On The Borderland. After a couple of minutes of scrambling around in the piles, I found a CD for £2.50 which, on the front, had a slightly blurred photo of Morrissey and the title "Beethoven Was Deaf". I turned it over to look at the track listing and immediately my eyes were drawn to "You're The One For Me Fatty". Seriously, was this bloke a genuine indie messiah or a very bad 1970's comedian? I carried on reading and found that this was a live album, which put me off buying it even more. I decided there and then that I definitely didn't like Morrissey and went to walk out of the shop. I stood in the doorway and remembered that the hippy who owned the shop would give customers £1.50 for any decent CD album, so if I returned this one after listening to it, and undoubtedly dismissing it as rubbish, it would in effect only cost me £1. For the sake of a quid, I thought I should buy it to confirm my apathy to the bequiffed one. Little did I know that buying that CD would cost me a lot more.

I paid for the CD, got the bus home and settled down in my

room to listen with an air of apathy and a can of Tizer.

I had read in The Guardian that researchers had found that heroin was the most addictive drug for the first time user. Those researchers had obviously never heard "Beethoven Was Deaf".

Within 10 minutes of putting the CD into the stereo I was entranced. Within an hour of constant listening I'd learnt enough of the lyrics to be able to croon along to the choruses, whilst throwing myself around my room with gay abandon. Songs like "Jack The Ripper" and "Glamorous Glue" sounded like they came from a different era to the indie-pop that I was used to listening to. His words were full of desire, wit and intrigue and I ate them all up.

As the afternoon became evening, I politely refused all offers of tea from Mum as I simply had to keep listening to the album. After 6 hours of playing the CD over and over and looking through the inlay booklet, I was in love with everything about him. The voice, the attitude, the look, the lyrics and the songs had tapped into a space in my brain that was previously listed as vacant. I was desperately in need of more songs but as the shops all shut at 5.30pm, I forlornly accepted that I would have to wait until the next morning to go and buy my next fix.

As I waited for morning to come, I decided to immerse myself further into the world of Morrissey by re-styling my hair. It quickly became obvious that my long Bernard Butleresque locks weren't going to be easily teased into a Morrissey style quiff. My sideburns, however, were almost in the Moz style anyway. I had been cultivating them since I was 13, first as hair slicked down in front of my ears and now, thanks to my weekly shave, closely resembling the stubbly real thing. I ended up having a shave at about 11pm, by torchlight so as not to wake anyone, just to try and make my sideburns look exactly like Morrissey's. I was already totally addicted.

I woke the next morning and made plans to skive off school in order to feed my new habit. The problem was that I had only £6.50 in my wallet. What I did have though, was my Building Society Savings Account passbook. Mum had made it clear to me on numerous occasions that this book was strictly only to be used to deposit money. That account hadn't seen a withdrawal since the day it was opened shortly after my birth. I'd had it drummed into me that my savings account would one day be used for something important. Well it seemed to me that day had arrived. I needed those albums.

Idly daydreaming on the bus journey into town, it dawned on me that not only did I need to buy all the Morrissey albums that I could find, but all The Smiths ones as well. This was all set to be a thrilling, if expensive, morning. I walked into the Building Society, handed over my passbook and quietly whispered "£100 withdrawal please". I'm not sure why I was whispering. Maybe I was concerned that they had my mum on speed-dial and would be secretly calling her with the news that I was daring to withdraw money from my own account.

I stashed the illicit bundle of £10 notes in the pocket of my Pepe jeans and ran to HMV. It's one of the best feelings imaginable when you are stood in a record shop with cash in your pocket and you know that you can spend it all on music that you are desperate to own. I was like Augustus Gloop let loose in Mr Wonkas factory. I couldn't have stopped myself from grabbing the Morrissey and Smiths CD's from the shelves if my life had depended on it. It was a compulsion. I had given control of my functions to the music of Morrissey and would have to live with whatever decisions it made on my behalf. I didn't buy all the albums I needed from HMV of course, not with their £12.99 for a non-chart CD policy. I shopped around in Andy's, Our Price and House on the Borderland and got the bus home with 3 Morrissey CD's (Viva Hate, Kill Uncle, Your Arsenal) and 5 Smiths CD's (The Smiths, Meat Is Murder, The Queen Is Dead, Strangeways Here We Come and Hatful of Hollow) tucked safely inside my rucksack. All for the princely sum of £91.50, which seemed like an outstanding deal to me. As the bus rumbled along, the adrenaline began to subside and it dawned on me that Mum probably wasn't going to see it the same way.

I got home and furtively opened the front door. After quickly scanning the kitchen for Mum's presence, I ran for my life up the stairs and hid the CD's under my bed. A doped up to the eyeballs Ben Johnson couldn't have beaten me in that 20 yard sprint. Mum didn't actually find out about the missing money until 6 months later when she went to pay some of my birthday money into the account and asked for a statement. She was not amused, and I was grounded for a week with the promise that I would pay back the money that I had "stolen" from myself. The albums were well worth it.

Of the 8 albums that I'd bought, "The Queen Is Dead" was the instant hit. How had I not heard this album before? I was the miserable juvenile with the dark sense of humour that needed these songs, and it was a need. Hearing songs like 'I Know It's Over' and 'There Is A Light...' for the first time was a call to arms to all of my repressed teenage emotions and they came tearing to the surface for a view of the brave new world. I knew that he had an army of fans, were they all like me? Knowing that we were all joined by this supernatural force that was Morrissey was a real comfort to my adolescent brain.

I wanted it all; CD's, live shows, t-shirts, videos; whatever I could get my hands on to quench my thirst. Within a matter of days of buying those albums, I had placed a trust in this man that I had never even met in the same way you would trust your dad or your best friend. In songs such as 'Cemetery Gates' and 'Suedehead' he lit up my life and was talking directly to me in the space under my desk in suburban Peterborough. The swelteringly hot spring and summer of 1993 were spent under that desk, feverishly gulping down every Morrissey song I could find. I took every word that he sang as gospel. Those lyrics instantly became the user-manual to my youth. For better or worse, this was it for me.

Within 3 weeks of welcoming Morrissey into my life, I had decided to become a vegetarian. I felt the need to show my total and utter commitment to him, and the best way to do that seemed to be to give up eating meat. His arguments in favour of embracing vegetarianism were compelling but, to be honest, if he had told me to give up all of my worldly possessions and go and live in a skip in Newport Pagnell, I would have been on the first train there. I was now a fully paid up member of the cult of Morrissey.

Even with Mum's backing, it wasn't easy being a vegetarian in 1993. I was, quite understandably, seen as a freak by my mates, but I did manage to convert my immediate family so that, within a few months, we were a meat free household. I knew, because he kept telling me, that my dad wasn't keen on "going veggie" but as Mum was the only one who cooked in our house, he didn't really have much choice. Then, like with most things that you do for a period of time it became a habit, something that Dad got used to.

My only concern in relation to Morrissey was the music press ascertion that his best days were behind him. Would I never get to hear a better album than "The Queen is Dead" or "Your Arsenal"?

Then, in 1994, he released 'Vauxhall & I' and upon hearing the opening line of 'Now My Heart Is Full', I moved from addiction to obsession. Everything about it was sublime, from the cover with Morrissey looking resplendent, to the passion filled tales packed within. It's an album that has all elements of life wrapped up within its immaculate tunes. The single that preceded the album, "The More You Ignore Me, The Closer I Get" set the charts alight (well it got to number 8 in the UK), and the dark wit and genius of that anthem was there for all to hear.

That album was released in March with my A-Level exams looming but, being the rebel that I was, I still spent far too much time listening to "Vauxhall & I". At least once a week, I would leave the house on the pretence of going to school, and then wait behind a huge bush at the end of our road for my parents to go to work, before sneaking back home and spending the day listening to those life affirming songs. I needed to know exactly what Moz was thinking on the key life subjects, from emotional rollercoasters (Now My Heart Is Full) to the need for your best mates ("Hold Onto Your Friends"). "Vauxhall & I" also helped cement my theory that the final track of any album should be it's best. This theory had worked with all my favourite albums, from The Stone Roses debut (I Am The Resurrection), The Charlatans "Some Friendly" (Sproston Green) through to Billy Braggs "Workers Playtime" (Waiting For the Great Leap Forwards). 'Vauxhall' had the gigantic epitaph that was "Speedway". From the sound of chainsaws at its opening to lyrics that felt as if Moz was singing whilst looking through the window into my soul. I would sit under my desk, idly pressing repeat on the remote control as the song glided to its conclusion, desperate to hear something new in the next listen, to feel even closer to the words and the melody.

Morrissey had also provoked the type of fluttering in my stomach that neither Tim Burgess or Belinda Carlisle had managed previously. I would sit for hours gazing at photos of him, wanting to reach out and hug him. I knew that I wasn't alone in feeling such emotions. I had seen video footage of grown men, many of whom no doubt had wives and girlfriends, hurl themselves onto the stage where Moz was singing, desperate to hug, kiss or caress the messiah. I spent a lot of the summer of 1993 exploring my sexuality in the confines of my bedroom. I would ponder why I found both Morrissey and Tim Burgess so physically attractive whereas, since Jo, I'd shown very little interest in the opposite sex.

I had vague thoughts about being gay without every really

believing that I was. In the pages of the NME, I was reading about ambiguous or bisexual indie popsters like Brett Anderson, without having a clue what either phrase meant in reality. That July, something happened which showed me with definitive certainty that I was not gay. It occurred during a raucous and particularly sweaty set by The Wedding Present at the Phoenix Festival. The crowd was tightly packed together as the band blasted through their set and I was throwing myself around with the best of them.

About halfway through "Blue Eyes", I noticed a hand pressed against the front of my jeans, on my crotch. At first I thought it was just an accident, someone inadvertently trying to find somewhere to put their hand in the packed crowd. I did my best to ignore it and jumped around as Gedge and co. banged out another tune. I started to change my opinion as, during the intro to "Silver Shorts", this errant hand began to force its way inside the front of my jeans. I froze, not so much out of terror, more out of a sense of "what the hell is happening here?" After a few seconds of this unwelcome foreplay, I turned my head to see who had their hand perilously close to my 2 day old festival pants.

I came face to face with a lad, with a Suede "Drowners" t-shirt on, who was probably in his early 20's;

Me: 'What the hell are you doing mate?'

Drowner: 'What you wanted me to do!'

Me: 'You what?'

Drowner: 'You've been grinding your arse against me for the last half hour, thrusting against me and brushing your arm against mine.'

Me: 'Fuck off. I wasn't doing anything, just dancing. I'm straight!'

Drowner: 'I'm bi-sexual....'

Me: 'Well not with me you're not.'

At this point the previously effeminate Suede fan suddenly recovered his guttural cockney accent and spat out:

Drowner: 'You prick-tease, you've led me on, I'll…'

At this point the world went dark. The Drowner had head-butted me and made good contact with the bridge of my nose. Thankfully, I had taken off my glasses and stored them in their case, in my shorts pocket. With the help of a kind young lady in a "James – Sit Down" t-shirt, I made my way out of the crush and flopped down in a sweaty, bloody heap at the back of the crowd. As the ringing in my ears slowly receded, I went back over what had just happened and happily concluded that I didn't deserve the "prick-tease" title that the Drowner had foisted upon me. I shook my head clear and showed an adolescents ability to get on with life by running back to my tent to get a clean t-shirt. I didn't want my mates to find out what had happened, so wiped the worst of the blood away with my now ruined Wedding Present '4' t-shirt. Looking in one of the girls make-up mirrors, I found that, miraculously, the mark on my nose was tiny and was covered almost entirely when I put my glasses back on. I pulled on my own Suede 'Drowners' t-shirt and jogged unsteadily back to the arena.

I got back just in time to see The Wedding Present leave the stage. Maff bounded over, wreathed in sweat and exclaimed "Bloody quality gig mate, weren't it!" I nodded my agreement and off we went to the bar to get a pint. I never discussed the incident with anyone and it didn't make me angry or vengeful, it was all just a bit odd.

Pyramid Stage at 1am

OUR summer was taken over by music festivals. We had decided way back in the depths of winter that we would make our first trip to the Glastonbury Festival.

We left Peterborough on the Thursday morning and arrived onsite in the middle of the afternoon. We managed to get the supreme camping spot, up on the hill by the Eavis farmhouse, looking down over the whole site. Maff's Dad, Rob, had driven a group of us to the festival and decided when we got there to climb over the flimsy perimeter fence and have a couple of days with us. Rob was a great bloke, he was the cool Dad that all of us wanted. All he did that weekend was watch the bands, have a drink and a laugh. He never tried to act like a teenager, he just loved the music.

Glastonbury was a special place. I fell for its charms from the second I got on site. By 1993 it certainly wasn't the hippy love-fest that it had been through the 1970's. Instead, we discovered that it was full of northern lads who had jumped over the perimeter fence without paying for a ticket and were determined to rid the world of its pharmaceuticals by Sunday lunchtime, at the very latest.

The festival was bathed in glorious sunshine and the bands that I'd wanted to see were on top form, with Teenage Fanclub followed by Suede lighting up the NME Stage on the Friday night. My sentimental side was in full flow and, as I looked around during Teenage Fanclub's glittering set of indie-pop, surrounded by my mates, with the sun setting, I thought, "This really is the best place in the world."

I wasn't one for spirituality, stone circles and crystals with positive energy, but found that when you're at Glasto you would need to have a swinging brick for a soul not to feel inspired. My favourite place on the site wasn't spiritual, it wasn't in one of the stone circles or even 4am in one of the rave fields. It was sat in front of the deserted Pyramid Stage. I had seen some beautiful sights in my life but nothing could compare to sitting with my back against that stage at 7am, looking back up the valley with the mist rolling down and watching the late night casualties trying to locate their tents. I couldn't get enough of the place and would go and sit in front of the stage as soon as I woke each day. I would then get mildly annoyed when it got to mid-morning and the festival would start to wake up and invade my quiet time.

I even had a quick fling at that Glasto'. I had known Sarah since we'd started secondary school. She had always been one of the girls in our little group but, to be honest, her intelligence and beauty meant that she should have been hanging around a better class of lads than us. From the first night at Glasto and our awkward drunken kiss, we both knew that we weren't going to have a relationship. It was to be a festival romance that would expire the second we left the site. We sat up talking rubbish about music, life and the future through Saturday night and as the dawn broke, I decided to invite her to experience my special place. We gathered up the last cans of Holsten Pils and took the long walk down the hill to the Pyramid, occasionally falling head first over guy ropes and wetting ourselves laughing. I felt on top of the world. Here I was, in what had quickly become my newly discovered favourite spot on the planet, drinking and giggling with a girl I fancied. We cuddled up against the stage barrier, masters of all that we surveyed.

That blissful scene lasted for about half an hour before Sarah got bored:

Sarah: 'How long are we going to sit here?'

Me: 'I normally sit here for hours at this time of the morning, it's an amazing view don't you think?'

Sarah: 'Not being funny Jay, but this is getting boring and I'm cold. I'm going back to the tent. Come on, come with me and we can warm up.'

Any sensible 16 year old lad would have realised what she had subtly suggested, and quickly agreed to follow.

Me: 'Nah, you're ok, I like it here. I'll sit here for a while yet.'

Shaking her head, Sarah stomped off back up the hill. That was the end of our fling.

I was still in front of the stage supping my first cup of tea of the day when she came back down the hill, a couple of hours later, to get some breakfast with Doody's girlfriend, Lisa. I knew they were giggling about me being sat there on my own but I didn't care. Then, just in case I was in any doubt, Lisa's foghorn voice broke the calm Somerset morning by cackling;

'Christ, Jay, you're a sad bastard.'

I figured that given our romance had ended at the Pyramid Stage, Sarah would no longer want to come with me to see the ever festival friendly Billy Bragg later on that Sunday. It was her loss.

Two weeks after Glastonbury '93 we went to the inaugural Phoenix Festival. Where Glasto had been a spiritual setting, Phoenix was what I imagined music festivals to be like in North Korea. Set on a disused military airfield at Long Marston, about 10 miles south of Stratford-Upon-Avon, each festival-goer was handed a leaflet at the entrance with a strict set of rules. We were told exactly where to camp, that no fires were allowed and that the arena would shut promptly at 11pm. None of these slightly petty rules would have been an insurmountable problem if they had provided some decent facilities. The problem was that we had to queue for everything all weekend, whether that be for a burger, a pint or a pee. Throughout the Thursday and Friday you could feel the tension building on the campsite, with large groups gathering to moan at nobody in particular about the lack of a bar and the rules that were being enforced by stewards who appeared to be inspired by the Sergeant Major from 'It Ain't Half Hot Mum'.

The main reason I had been looking forward to going to Phoenix was a 2nd stage headline slot from Billy Bragg. At 9pm on the Saturday night, he walked out onto the stage and said "Hope you're all in a singalong mood!", before 5000 people joined him in a mass rendition of "To Have and To Have Not". It was a party atmosphere that night as Billy and his band produced exquisite versions of "Sexuality" and "Cindy of a Thousand Lives" for the crowd to sway along to. I was there with Maff, who had become my Phoenix buddy, and we joyously danced along to the tunes as they spilled out. Billy must have also thought it was a cracking gig as, a few months later, he released a recording of it as an official bootleg called "No Pop, No Style, Strictly Roots".

After the bands finished on the Saturday night, the masses were unceremoniously marched out of the main arena at 10.45pm by the crack team of stewards cum bouncers. We dutifully made our way back to our tent and cracked open a bottle of Pink Lady to celebrate Billy's brilliance.

Within half an hour we could hear the shouts of defiance from folk all over the site and the unmistakable sound of glasses being smashed. My first reaction was, 'Ohhhh you're not allowed to bring any glass onto this site, they'll be in trouble'. We stood up to get a better view just in time to see a telegraph pole being torn down and then used as an impromptu but effective battering ram to knock down the entrance to the main arena. A guttural roar of celebration broke out amid shouted confirmation that it was 'a fuckin' riot' going on. At midnight, Maff and I went for a wander to see if anywhere in this totalitarian state masquerading as a festival was still serving food and ended up getting tacked onto the end of this rural riot. We stumbled around the darkness of the main arena, parts of which were being illuminated by fires set by the rioters. We weren't the kind of lads that wanted to smash things up so, despite being urged by the ubiquitous white blokes with dreadlocks to "Rip this place apart man", we soon got bored and went back to the only food stall that had remained open, smiled slyly at the lack of a queue, got some chips and went and sat up on the hill watching the scene play out.

As the fires burnt and the once aggressive stewards awaited the arrival of the police to quell the seething anger of the rebellious youths, my only concern was that my mum might see the scenes on the news and have her worst fears about festivals confirmed once and for all. Despite being only two weeks away from my 17th birthday, Mum was still very much in control of my future festival going destiny.

When we got back from Phoenix, Doody, Shin, Mark and I decided that the indie-pop world needed shaking up and decided to form a band. We figured that being in a band was a rite of passage for any music loving juveniles looking to grow up but we were particularly bad. None of us could play an instrument but we'd read about the punk ethos of just picking up a guitar and playing it so thought we would give it a go. Yet again I secretly raided my Building Society Savings Account and bought myself a 2nd hand bass guitar, 10W Amp and a microphone. Mark and Doods both bought guitars and amps from the local music shop, whilst Shin got himself a set of the yellowest drums I had ever seen.

It was only after we bought all the equipment and had our

first rehearsals that we realised that the punks were lying or were too drunk on cheap cider to care. In order to make some half decent music you needed to learn how to play your instruments. That seemed like far too much hard work to us.

Like all good teenage bands, the vast majority of our time was spent on choosing a name. After much debate we decided on "Mooncat". Mooncat was a puppet, of a cat, who came from the moon, funnily enough. He appeared in various kids TV shows in the early 1980's and it seemed a suitably twee name for an indie band.

The rest of our spare time that autumn was spent on Mooncat. We would attempt to write songs, learn our instruments and, most importantly, bond as a band. In reality, this meant spending Sunday afternoons in Shin's dads freezing cold garage, drinking Southern Comfort and discussing how long it would be before we would be ready to headline Glastonbury. We didn't get round to playing any gigs, we knew we weren't good enough for that but it was bloody good fun being in a band with my mates, dreaming of being indie-pop stars.

Mooncat split up in December of 1993, not through musical differences but because it was too cold to sit in that garage any longer. We had gone as far as we could as a band.

1994

Britpop Is Mine

1994 was, musically, the best of my life. It seemed that almost every week another amazing single or album was released and, with Glastonbury and plenty of gigs thrown in, it couldn't get any better. It seemed incredible to me that Blur's "Parklife" and Pulp's "His 'n' Hers" were released in the same month (April). These were albums that I adored from the first listen. Add in Oasis "Definitely Maybe" (released in August), The Charlatans "Up To Our Hips" (March) and of course Morrissey's "Vauxhall & I" (March), and you had 5 of my favourite albums ever right there, in that 5 month period.

Those albums also helped me to expand my music collection back into the 1960's. When Tim Burgess and Damon Albarn talked of The Small Faces and The Kinks, I went out and bought up their cheap £3.99 greatest hits albums, which always featured some badly recorded live tracks. Even my dad approved of me howling along to songs like 'Afterglow' and 'Waterloo Sunset' in my room, as they were 'proper music'.

Pulp's seminal "His 'n' Hers" was an album of nylon based beauty and was a constant in the CD tray of my stereo. I had discovered Pulp thanks to their "Razzmatazz" single the previous year which, upon its release, was the 99p CD single of the week in Andy's Records. We had been to see them play at

Northampton Roadmenders in 1993, supported by an energetic and gloriously shambolic Elastica. From that night onwards Jarvis Cocker was right up there in the exalted company of my heroes. He was the geek anti-hero that all us indie kids wanted to be. He gave us all hope that us nerds could make it as a popstar in the 1990's.

"His 'n' Hers" boasted one of the best singles of the era in "Babies". It was sparkling pop, with its tale of suburban sex and hiding in wardrobes. Songs like 'Joyriders' and 'Pink Glove' would flow out of my stereo every evening after school with me throwing my Jarvis shapes and Dad shouting that I would; 'Go through the bloody floor dancing like an idiot to that rubbish'.

The Charlatans latest slab of effortless cool was packed full of melodic, Hammond-driven mod influenced rock 'n' roll. "Up To Our Hips" t-shirts became my gig uniform, and Doody, Jacko and I got to see another landmark Charlatans gig at Trentham Gardens in Stoke that April. I was a Charlatan for life.

It wasn't all about newly released epic albums that spring though. On 5th April, I tuned in to the Radio 1 Evening Session expecting Steve Lamacq and Jo Whiley to be playing the latest indie tunes to be met with the news that Kurt Cobain had killed himself. That was a bit of a downer when all I'd wanted to hear was the new Primal Scream single. It was a shame though, as I had finally started liking some of Nirvana's songs on "In Utero", in particular the gorgeously bleak "Heart Shaped Box". I was sad that he'd died but I didn't go out and buy a Dennis the Menace style jumper, a pair of Converse boots and suddenly start telling everyone how I wanted to move to Seattle. I had Britpop on my mind.

The two albums that changed the Britpop scene and propelled it firmly into the mainstream were "Parklife" and "Definitely Maybe". Blur were the established indie band who had gone from baggy with their first album (Leisure) through to mod with their second (Modern Life Is Rubbish), and had found a magic formula with their third (Parklife). It was packed full of blistering tunes that would get nightclub dancefloors jumping (Girls and Boys) or bring you down to earth with a loving bump (Badhead). It was the first Britpop album to really crossover and make the leap into the mainstream. The vast majority of the people that bought "Parklife" weren't geeky like me when it came to indie they just recognised great pop tunes and wanted to listen to them over that long hot summer of 1994.

From an early Oasis live session on The Evening Session in February, I was hooked. They were the gang of lads, making rock 'n' roll tunes that spoke to us, the band that the times needed. I cut a huge picture of Noel and Liam out of the NME, stuck it on my bedroom wall and wrote on it in marker pen "The Best Fuckin' Rock N Roll Band In The World". That lasted about a week before my dad spotted it, ordered me to take it down and advised me, not for the first time, that "When you have your own house, you can put whatever you want up on the walls".

I'd just turned 18 when "Definitely Maybe" was released, and it was like a hurricane blowing into my brain. It smashed to smithereens everything that I thought I knew about indie music. It was an album that I carried around with me, often singing the words to 'Columbia' without realising, as I walked down the street. I had to have it close to me at all times. I knew it wasn't ground-breaking in the sense that Noel wore his influences like a badge of honour, but his songs were the unifying force of that summer. I would stand in my room, (it wasn't an album you could sit down and listen to) and screech along to "Live Forever" and "Supersonic". It wasn't subtle or smart but it was glorious, life defining music to my teenage ears. They were the band that I'd been waiting for. The Stone Roses debut had me spellbound but I was too young to be at Spike Island or experience the buzz of that album when it was released. For "Definitely Maybe", I was smack bang in the middle of it at the perfect age and I bought into the cult of Oasis with every penny and ounce of sweat that I possessed.

Despite being loved by the indie hordes, Oasis were never really an indie band. From the first listen, whether you liked their music or not, it was obvious that they were going to be huge. "Supersonic" was a cracking debut single, and I sat in front of our TV on a Saturday morning and watched Noel and Liam in the video on the Chart Show, looking effortlessly fuck off cool. Afterwards I ran upstairs, put the CD single on the stereo, stood ram-rod straight, with feet at ten to two and my chin pointing upwards like a baby giraffe searching for food and sang along at the top of my voice.

I was lucky enough to see them twice that year, once at Glastonbury and then in the week that "Whatever" hit the charts in December, at Cambridge Corn Exchange. I had passed my driving test a couple of months before the gig, and Dad agreed to lend me his trusty Vauxhall Cavalier so that I could drive my mates to the venue. In the week leading up to the gig the weather was atrocious and on the afternoon of what was a key day in my entire life, Mum decided that I "couldn't drive the car as it's too icy out there". I decided, in a fit of blind panic at potentially missing the gig, to show some Gallagher attitude of my own and ignore her. I waited until she went into the front room, grabbed the keys, ran out to the car and went to pick up Doody and Jacko. I was going to see the band that were set to define my generation. I knew that I didn't want to have to look my kids in the eye years later and admit that I missed seeing Oasis in the early days because my mum had told me that I couldn't go.

Oasis were superb that night, at their nonchalant best and the crowd lapped it up. We jumped up and down in a tangled mass of wild abandon. Everyone in the place appeared to surge towards the stage as they launched into 'Cigarettes & Alcohol', desperate to be a part of the night, to be as close to these indie-rock gods as possible. Lads who were presumably drunk or high were jumping the 20ft from the seating area down into the standing section to get closer to the action. It was a very special night, with 1500 people rocking the foundations of the old place. It was more than worth the bollocking from Mum and her pledge to never let me use Dads' car again.

For those electrifying few months, my dedication to Oasis was at the same level as my dedication to Morrissey. I couldn't get enough of them, the spirit, the tunes, their effect on the indie world that we lived in.

It was also a massive year for me for reasons other than music. I just about passed my A-Levels in the summer. I put my D in English Literature squarely down to almost passing out with excitement when seeing the exam paper had what I thought was the ideal question on George Orwell. His novels and essays had become my reading of choice over the previous 18 months and he had done as much as Billy Bragg in shaping my political and social views. Unfortunately, in my feverish state, I produced the most childlike fan boy rubbish excuse for an exam essay ever committed to paper. I may as well have just written "I love George Orwell" on the paper and walked out of the room.

I took the decision, along with Jacko, to defer my place at University and to take a gap year. I was chuffed, and quite surprised, that Cardiff had accepted me on to their BSc Social Policy course, so was quite happy to string out the unfamiliar glow of achievement for another year before actually starting the course.

Most folk take such a year to go and explore the world, see new things and have amazing experiences. I got a temporary job with the local life assurance company, inputting standing order mandates for £4 an hour.

Jacko and I were both sick of being skint so our gap year plan was to earn as much as we could whilst also going out for a few drinks at the weekends. We would then go to the summer music festivals before heading to Europe for a month of inter-railing. We weren't setting ourselves very high targets but we achieved everything we set out to in that year and that's not something I could say about many other years.

1994 was also the year that, after 18 months without regular employment, my teenage hormones clocked on again. The year began with a brief fling with a girl in our 6th form called Nicola, who after a few weeks with me decided that she was better off going back to her ex-boyfriend. It was never going to work between us, she didn't really like music of any kind and loved spending her weekends in the nightclubs up town. I, on the other-hand, had taken to spending any spare time I had listening to 30 year old Johnny Cash recordings to supplement my musical diet. When she packed me in, one cold and wet Friday evening stood outside her house, I simply smiled sweetly, got on my bike and went home to listen to "Live At San Quentin".

As the Britpop spring sprang into summer I did something that I had never done before, I got together with one of my mates ex-girlfriends. Mark and Kate had been together for a couple of teenage years, which were roughly as long as dog years. They had been blissfully happy during the majority of their time together, with Mark even missing some Posh home games to spend time with her. I, more than anyone, would absolutely slate him for putting a girl before our football club. Going to the match was what we did as a group of mates, it was our thing, and I didn't see it as growing up in any way to ditch that for spending time with a girl.

They were the golden couple of our group, as couples crashed and burned around them, they just kept going. But like 99% of epic, seemingly unending, teenage love affairs, it didn't last. Mark was heading off to university in the autumn. He was determined to get out of my beloved home city, he had outgrown it and was all set to make his own way in life away from Kate and his old mates. They came up with the standard adolescent statement that it was a mutual decision to split up but none of us believed that. I understood why he was doing it but it still smacked my feelings against my ribcage knowing that one of my best mates couldn't wait to get away. Mark and I were close mates, bound together by a mutual love of sitting in darkened bedrooms and listening to music, without feeling the need for too much conversation. Although it was a little weird, and went against several unwritten rules, it made Kate and I getting together all the more obvious. He was leaving us behind, and knowing that we were both going to miss him, we clung to each other for comfort.

Not that Kate and I ever discussed Mark or their relationship. We were 18 years old in the summer of Britpop; we had much better things to do. There were albums to buy, bottles of her mums Chardonnay to swipe from the fridge and then extremely quiet, slightly tipsy sex to be had in her bedroom so that her parents, who were asleep in the next room, didn't hear.

Kate was a pretty girl without ever realising it and I found that really attractive. We had been friends, through Mark, for a couple of years and slipped easily into being a couple. We knew each other that well it was easy. It wasn't full of love or desire or excitement about the future, it was just easy for both of us. That summer was shaping up to be a truly great one and we had made a logical decision to be together through those experiences. We would sit in her bedroom, or occasionally mine, and listen to all the new music that was being released and chat about where we saw our lives going. We were close and we cared about each other, but never remotely came close to falling in love.

Never Use Morrissey Lyrics To
End a Relationship

OUR main topic of conversation when quaffing stolen wine was the upcoming Glastonbury and the glorious time that we would spend watching bands, drinking and sleeping under canvas in a 2 man tent. Not that Kate and I were due to share a tent though as I always co-habited with Jacko at festivals. He was my best mate, and I wasn't about to turf him out of my tent just because I had a new girlfriend.

Glasto 1994, was everything I'd hoped for and much more. It was the best festival that I'd been to by an absolute mile. With the sun beating down, a group of 12 of us, most of whom had just finished their A-Levels, spent a weekend making memories. Even a serious kid such as I could relax and let the days just wash over me with a smile on my face and a pint in my hand. You couldn't get a paper onsite so we didn't know any news or events for the 4 days we were there and that was amazingly liberating. We really didn't have a care in the world.

Some of our group went to Glasto for the atmosphere, the spirituality, the sex and drugs but for me it was always about the rock 'n' roll. I spent hours in the build up to the festival endlessly reworking my personal timetable, and then learning it off by heart. I didn't have time to waste looking at programmes and timetables whilst I was at the festival, it all had to be committed to memory. I had to know that if someone asked me who I was going to see on the Saturday at 8pm, I would instantly be able to say with absolute certainty: "Bjork". Along with every other indie-boy on the planet, I had developed a huge crush on Bjork since her "Debut" album was released. Unfortunately, when I got onsite and saw the actual stage times, I discovered that part of her set clashed with Weller's on the Pyramid. As usual, I put a man with a guitar before a beautiful woman.

My personal Saturday timetable had the name "Paul Weller" as the must see. I had fallen hook, line and sinker for the Weller revival that had come about thanks to his majestic "Wild Wood" album. It was an album that got deep into my DNA and would have to be listened to at least once a day. To songs like "Sunflower" and "The Weaver" I would stand in my bedroom singing along, shaking my hair and jutting my chin out in the Weller style.

I was the only one of our gang that wanted to see The Modfather so I made my way down to the front of the crowd at the Pyramid Stage for his slot. You could just wander down to the front 5 minutes before any act began their set and I managed to get myself almost onto the stage barrier to await his arrival.

Weller was on fire that night, banging out all his tunes with an edge and passion that got the ever increasing crowd on his side. As the sun finally set on the sweltering June evening, watching Weller play "The Weaver", I wouldn't have wanted to be anywhere else in the world. I genuinely thought that life couldn't get any better as my brain set its camera to automatic and took hundreds of mental images.

I wandered the site on my own into the early hours swigging from my paper cup which a very kind lad, whacked off his nut on E, had insisted in filling to the pint line with Southern Comfort and lemonade. I must have looked like a gurning simpleton myself, walking around with a huge grin on my face, before taking residence outside a Joe Banana's Blanket Stall, where the skull grinding techno from their sound system lulled me to sleep on the dewy grass.

The Sunday at Glasto that year went straight into the top 3 days of my life chart. Kate and I had started it with a quick sleeping bag fumbling whilst Jacko was out getting his essential early morning cuppa. I then spent the day stood in a field with the sun shining down, with my mates, my girlfriend and her mates, having a drink and watching the best single day line-up that I think a UK festival had ever seen. The NME stage line-up that Sunday included:

(in order of appearance, from headliner down)

Spiritualized

Blur

Radiohead

Inspiral Carpets

Pulp

Chumbawamba

Credit To The Nation

Oasis

Echobelly

Taking aside Chumbawamba (but not the criminally underrated Credit To The Nation), that was my musical year, right there in one day on one stage.

At 2pm, Liam Gallagher walked out onto the stage on this sweltering day in a jumper, sunglasses and swigging from a can of Red Stripe. He surveyed the expectant masses with disdain, Noel's guitar kicked in and Oasis ripped the field to shreds. The crowd were ecstatic, singing back to Liam the words to songs that were still months away from being released. I danced like I was wired to the mains, clad in my classic black Oasis logo t-shirt, and didn't want it to end. Everyone in that packed Somerset field knew that this band of ruffians were all set for world domination.

Pulp were at their best in the middle of the afternoon. Their tales of bedrooms and hiding in wardrobes shouldn't have worked in the sunshine, but Jarvis and co. always knew how to put on a peerless show. While the rest of the festival was clad in the obligatory shorts and band t-shirt, Jarvis walked on stage sporting huge 1970's sunglasses and wrapped in a corduroy jacket and spent the next 45 minutes with an enthralled crowd hanging on his every yelp and scissor kick. My only regret of that weekend was, by staying to watch Pulps set, I only got to see 5 minutes of the legend that was Johnny Cash on the Pyramid Stage.

The Inspiral Carpets kept the indie vibe rolling along through the afternoon with the best of their "Devil Hopping" album and singles like "Dragging Me Down" and "This Is How It Feels". We then witnessed a breathtaking set from Radiohead, during which Thom Yorke appeared to be undertaking psychological therapy by screaming his lyrics at the crowd. We cheered and clapped, for want of not knowing what else to do, whilst this tortured genius went about his art, before getting a beer from the bar and settling down for the evening's main event.

Blur were riding the crest of "Parklife's" success and Albarn sucked up the joyous acclaim of the Glasto' faithful with the gusto of someone having their first drink on an all-inclusive holiday. Their set was a celebration for band and crowd alike and was joyous to watch and be a part of. As the sun set over the site, the band rattled through "Parklife", with thousands of fans bouncing and swaying as appropriate. It was an extra special performance, a gig where you grabbed hold of your mates for the singalong tunes, then shared a hug with your girlfriend to the quieter ones and all felt right with the world.

After having our retina's scorched by Spiritualized's light show, I was determined to hold onto the feeling of having the world at the end of my Adidas Sambas for as long as possible, so wandered the festival site with Maff and Jacko, drinking into the small hours, taking in everything this tented civilisation could offer from the late night raves to the stone circle, via the left field stage. Kate had, sensibly, gone back to the tent for a kip as we were set to begin the journey home at 4am. We had travelled in a minibus driven by Frank, the 22 year old boyfriend of one of the girls from our school who was also at the festival. The plan was that we would begin the long journey back to Peterborough in the middle of the night in order to beat the traffic.

At 3am, I went for one last sit in front of the Pyramid Stage on my own, wondering if I would ever have another weekend as good as this one. Before my serenity lead to the inevitable sleep takeover, I stumbled back up the hill to wake Kate and pack away our tent. As I'd consumed plenty of Carlsberg, some herbal highs we'd bought off a Scouser and hadn't slept since Saturday, as soon as the minibus began to trundle off site, I fell soundly asleep across Kate's lap.

I must have been knackered because, when our minibus crashed into the motorway central reservation, I remained asleep. Kate had to shake me awake to make sure that I hadn't smacked my head and been knocked out. I awoke to lots of tears from the girls, Jacko sat white as a sheet gripping the seat in front of him, and shouted apologies from a shaken up Frank. I assumed that he had fallen asleep at the wheel and we had somehow contrived to avoid certain death but, to be honest, I was too drunk and high on life to care too much. Thankfully, nobody was hurt so with minimal damage to the mini-bus and a couple of strong cups of coffee for Frank at the nearby service station, we set off on our way again. I went back to sleeping peacefully for the remainder of the journey.

When I got home and Mum asked me "How was it all?" I gave her my now stock returning from a festival response; everything had gone well, we'd had fun, not drunk too much and of course not taken any drugs. I failed to mention the minibus crash. I may have been only a month away from my 18th birthday and the tantalising freedoms that theshold had to offer, but I didn't want to take any chances where Mum was concerned.

Kate and I were in the midst of a summer that was full of sunshine and hours spent locked in her room after her mum and dad had gone to the pub. We were becoming adept at making each other smile but we both knew that deep down she still loved Mark and that I only really loved Morrissey. I would find a way to bring Moz into any conversation, from; What would Morrissey think to the news stories of the day through to debating which Smiths album we should play whilst we explored each other's teenage appetites.

We would openly talk about our futures, but never our future. We knew that we didn't have one. Something or someone was going to come along and tempt one of us away from this life of festivals, sun and sex. As summer turned to autumn, I thought our relationship was getting boring and decided that I wanted out. Being an obsessive, who wanted Moz to influence every nook and cranny of my life, I couldn't simply tell Kate that.

I was a bastard to Kate. She was a lovely girl who had always been nothing but considerate and kind to me. I'd got bored and suddenly found myself wanting to be on my own again for no real reason other than that I listened to too much Morrissey and thought that being in this enjoyable easy-going relationship wasn't what Moz would have wanted for me. Where was the complicated element of this relationship, other than Kate still loving one of my best mates? Where was the heartbreak and the drama? One wet September evening, I sat Kate down on her bed and gave her the old flannel about "it's not you, it's me", made an exaggerated show of giving her a long, slow kiss on the lips and walked out of her house. That was it, we were over. I had taken on Morrissey's vegetarianism, sideburns and now thought it a good idea to paint myself as someone who was "better off alone". I walked out of her life, leaving her a note which contained lines from Moz's "Will Never Marry" as I disappeared up my own arse.

Kate got the last laugh though as within a week of splitting up with her, I realised that I'd made a mistake. She told me that she just wanted to be mates now and finished our chat with, "To be honest your Morrissey obsession is weird and was beginning to freak me out a bit". Kate moved on and I spent the next 6 weeks trying unsuccessfully to persuade her to sleep with me again. It turned out that Morrissey couldn't satisfy all of my teenage urges.

The rest of 1994 was spent alternating between enjoying life, which usually involved me jumping round my room listening to "Strangeways Here We Come" or worrying about what the future might hold. This usually involved turning off the light, crawling into the space under my desk and listening to "Vauxhall & I" on repeat. Whatever mood I was in, Moz had the tunes to help or, indeed, hinder.

Now that we had a few quid in our pockets thanks to our gainful employment, my mates decided that it was a good time for us to start going up town on a Saturday night. If this had meant going to the only indie club in the city I would have been happy but it didn't. My mates wanted to go to nightclubs and make drunken attempts to cop off with members of the opposite sex. I liked the early evening drinking in the pubs, playing at being adults, having a laugh and a chat but the move into the clubs at 11pm filled me with dread. I hated the delights that Peterborough's clubs; Rinaldos, Shanghai Sams and 5th Avenue had to offer. My night would invariably go downhill as I passed the bouncers on the door and entered my vision of hell. Inside the darkened rooms would be lads and girls my age and beyond looking to couple off, dance to "Saturday Night" by Whigfield and drink overpriced bottled lager. I hated it. I didn't fit in. I didn't want to fit in.

While my mates were off dancing with girls or, on occasion, very mature women, I would find the quietest, darkest corner and sulk. I would often have to move quickly when a newly formed couple would hunt out a quiet dark corner to fornicate and would stumble into mine. I wasn't trying to be cool or ironic or smart, I just hated the places.

The best of our nights came in October when Blur played at Alexandra Palace, supported by Pulp and Supergrass. The landscape was changing, we were on the journey to watching indie bands in huge arenas but that night felt new, unique, another confirmation that Blur, one of our bands, had really made it. Jacko and I jumped around to our hearts content, safe in the knowledge that this Britpop high would last forever.

Despite the plethora of wasted Saturday nights, 1994 had been a cracking year, and it ended with the return of The Stone Roses. The five year wait from the Roses universally acclaimed debut album to their second long-player was agonising. Much of the indie world had moved on and got bored waiting for them to return. I, on the other hand, counted down the days on the calendar until "Second Coming" was released on 5th December. I took the day off work and was outside HMV waiting for them to unlock the doors so that I could be the first person in the city to get my hands on the album. I ran into the shop as they pulled the heavy front door open, despite the fact that they hadn't turned the lights on. I just went running into the darkness to find the album, much to the amusement of the staff.

"Second Coming" is one of the most underrated albums ever made. It was easy and fashionable to say, upon its release, that it was a pale imitation of their debut but it was a monster. Songs like "Ten Storey Love Song" and" Tightrope" would have been right at home on their debut album. In fact "Ten Storey

Love Song" quickly became my favourite Stone Roses tune of them all. Listening to that album on constant repeat was my Christmas holiday period sorted.

1995

I Started Something . . .

I RARELY made New Year's resolutions but my resolution for 1995 was quite simple – to grow up.

I spent the first couple of months diligently playing at being an adult by taking every hour of overtime that was available at work in order to save some money. I would then join up with my mates and go up town on Friday and Saturday nights, get drunk and repeat the dismal nightclub scenario. On weekday evenings I would sit at home listening to "Vauxhall & I" or "Second Coming" and daydream about the adventures that the second half of the year was set to bring, with a sense of anticipation and apprehension.

On February 9th, I finally got to see Morrissey play live. We were back at the Cambridge Corn Exchange, and I had been excited for weeks waiting for the evening to tick around. I knew that seeing him would be another step on the journey that had started 2 years earlier in House On The Borderland. As he strode onto the stage to the ecstatic roar of the crowd, I think I might have screamed like the girls in the 1960's film clips swept up in the hysteria of Beatlemania. I had lost control of my bodily functions, becoming a blurred whirl of arms and legs as he thundered into "Billy Budd". By five songs in and as the intro to "The More You Ignore Me..." rattled the foundations of the venue, the crowd treated the song like a long lost friend and grown men were suddenly throwing themselves over our heads, desperately grasping for the messiah. I spent most of that gig in a giddy haze, dazed and manically giggling at the fact that he was only 50 yards away from where I was stood. Finales to gigs just can't any better than "Now My Heart is Full", "Speedway", and then The Smiths classic "Shoplifters of the World Unite" as the closer. I lost my mates and a trainer in the desperate crush of "Shoplifters...", hugging complete strangers, feeling the love from the stage and from my fellow addicts. Coming out of the Corn Exchange that night, I was higher than the sun.

Seeing him live was the final piece of the jigsaw, I now felt part of the Moz gang. I had the tour t-shirt, the cut lip and bruised shin from the crowd frenzy and the ticket-stub that took pride of my place in my gig scrapbook. I had arrived.

In March, when the spring sun began to shine, I became the ultimate 18 year old cliché by starting a relationship with a 16 year old girl. Jess and I got talking at the bar of the Shamrock Club, while I waited patiently to be served a round of Newcy Brown Ales, (the only drink they couldn't water down) as she used her impish charm to push to the front of the queue. As we waited, I found myself using quite probably the most pathetic chat-up line ever; 'Quality (Oasis) shirt, have you seen them play yet? We saw them twice last year, fucking sweet man, really sweet'. Rather than run away from such banal chat, she returned the t-shirt compliment with a knowing nod to my Moz tour shirt and the conversation flowed. It was only at the end of the night, after a sweaty dance to The Lemonheads cover of 'Mrs Robinson', and the exchange of phone numbers that she revealed our age differential. By then I was hooked, and drunk, so decided to ignore our birth certificates and the inevitable piss-taking that would come from my mates.

Jess and I spent the next week talking on the phone in the evenings (local calls were free after 6pm) and then the next weekend sitting in the park, deciding to be boyfriend and girlfriend and kissing. She was a really pretty girl with dark hair and pale blue eyes, a nascent admiration for The Smiths and a shy smile that made my indie-boy heart flutter. Looks-wise she was in the league above me but she loved indie music and I imagine that the fact that I knew a fair bit about that particular subject was what attracted her. I knew that my photographic memory of Glastonbury line-up's would impress a girl one day and Jess was that girl.

As Jess was under (and didn't look) 18, we didn't go out to pubs or clubs other than the Shamrock who were happy to sell their watered down beer to anyone that simply said that they were old enough. We spent most of March sat in a park just outside the city centre, talking about music. Finally I had found someone who was happy to sit and listen to my ramblings about Morrissey for hours at a time. We never went to her house, due to the fact that her dad wasn't impressed by the 2 year age gap, but we occasionally went back to mine to listen to music. My dad was concerned about me starting a new relationship so close to going to university. I think he was worried that I would fall madly in love, refuse to go to Cardiff and stay at home. In reality that was never an option but it didn't stop him being paranoid about it. One afternoon, Jess and I were up in my room listening to The Smiths when Dad came home from work unexpectedly early. He could hear us sniggering so came barging in to find us fully clothed apart from me not having any socks on. Despite my protestations, he was sure that we had been "up to something" but, upon hearing him come in, had managed to both get dressed and appear calm, all apart from my lack of socks which were apparently a "dead giveaway". I couldn't wait to get to university, and not have to worry about whether I wanted to invite a different girl every night back to my room. I knew that I wouldn't be taking a different girl back to my room every night, I might well invite them but I knew they wouldn't come. It didn't occur to me that having such a thought probably wasn't a good omen for my nascent relationship with Jess.

"Strangeways Here We Come" had become my favourite Smiths album. Of course, "The Queen Is Dead" is 10 tracks of Morrissey/Marr genius, but 'Strangeways...' could make me laugh, cry and feel euphoric all in the course of one listen. It's an album packed with Morrissey's twisted black humour and some of the very best tunes that Johnny Marr had ever composed. I would play it to Jess constantly and rave about a different track on each listen, from 'Girlfriend in a Coma' to the delectable tale that is 'Paint a Vulgar Picture'. She would sit quietly in my room listening both to the album and to me, and smile. It is possible that Jess didn't like "Strangeways....." at all. I simply didn't give her enough space in any conversation we had, to talk about anything other than The Smiths.

I was constantly trying to dig my life deeper into the pit of twisted, unrequited love that Morrissey inhabited. I read Oscar Wilde despite only understanding the meaning of one sentence in every three. I would sit for hours watching home recorded VHS copies of films like "Kathy Come Home" because I knew that they had inspired Moz, and wanted them to have the same effect on my teenage bones. I liked the film but it was a bit bleak, which, I just about realised, was exactly the point.

When Jess wasn't around, I would stand in front of the stereo in my room and dance through the 1min 54 seconds intro to "Last Night I Dreamt That Somebody Loved Me" before throwing myself across the room and singing the lyrics to an imaginary crowd. "Strangeways...." was taking over my life and I bloody loved it.

In mid April, having answered an advert in the Education section of The Guardian, I was offered a 3 month job at a fee paying school in Hereford teaching 6-12 year olds how to play football and learn to swim in exchange for £55 per week with free board and lodgings thrown in. I accepted the job with the thought that being paid money to teach kids to play football essentially made me a professional coach, and I couldn't wait to go and live that particular dream.

The only issue I had to tackle was my fledgling relationship with Jess. The 140 miles between Peterborough and Hereford coupled with a combination of my not having a car and it being a bloody awful train journey meant that I wasn't going to be coming home very often during my coaching stint. It was however, far too good an opportunity to turn down. So with a quick hug and a promise to write to or call Jess every day, I was off to Hereford.

I loved Hereford, it was a beautiful, welcoming city with a rich history as well as some cracking pubs. I was on my own with money in my pocket and being paid to coach sport for 4 hours a day. In all honesty I didn't really think about Jess at all, I didn't have time. If I wasn't coaching I was sat on the balcony of my flat, which overlooked the cathedral grounds, listening to music or down the pub with the school's priest. Father James was in his late 20's, loved a drink and could talk for Ireland about football and music. We would pop out to the pub at least a couple of times a week and sit in there talking and supping until chucking out time. The next morning I would be stood at the back of the assembly hall trying not to let the Headmaster see how hungover I was. Up at the front, Father James would be singing hymns far too loudly and telling the kids another cleverly disguised tale about morality.

Hereford was also my first interaction with posh people. I was informed by the Headmaster that the school was well regarded among the upper echelons of British society. At the summer parents evening, the school held a wine and cheese reception "on the lawn". At such evenings at my old school, parents didn't get so much as a cup of tea and here I was, sipping vintage wine and eating canapés. I stood on the edge of the assembled group, gulping down the wine like it was squash, trying to hold my nerve, hoping that none of the parents would seek out my opinion on their children's footballing or swimming ability. Slowly but surely they wandered over for a chat and I was surprised to find that everyone I got introduced to asked me what school I went to. Unsurprisingly, none of the parents at this elite establishment had heard of Stanground College. Many of the parents and teachers were wearing their old school tie, whereas I was wearing the tie that came free with the shirt that I'd bought from Burtons earlier that afternoon.

Towards the end of my time in Hereford, I took a long weekend off work to join my mates in our now annual pilgrimage to Glastonbury. We knew it was the end of an era in our lives, as Jacko and I would be heading off to university that autumn. The two of us and Doody were therefore even more determined than usual to have a top weekend and with the likes of Oasis, The Charlatans, The Prodigy, Elastica and PJ Harvey in the line-up, the stage was set.

Aside from our mate Borgs tagging along, it was just the 3 of us at a festival for the first time, no girlfriends, no big group of friends and hangers-on. It was scorching hot and we had the time of our lives, living the weekend without even caring if the world outside those fields of green had ceased to exist. Life consisted of music, laughing, drinking, eating, dancing and occasionally sleeping. A magnificent weekend with my best mates in the world. Borgs was at his first ever festival and, having come to Somerset with £25 in his pocket, proceeded to spend £15 on a commemorative "Oasis – Glastonbury 1995" t-shirt. Faced with only having a tenner left for the weekend, he went into Pilton Village later that day and came back with the essential festival survival kit, namely 8 cans of Fosters, a baguette and a block of cheese.

Glastonbury 1995 saw Oasis rise from a 2pm slot on the NME Stage the previous year to Friday night Pyramid Stage headliners. It was a meteoric ascent, but one that we all assumed the Gallagher brothers would take in their stride. They strutted onto the stage in the requisite cocksure manner but, as dynamic as they had been the previous year, their set now felt leaden and boring. They played a whole batch of new songs that didn't sound anywhere near the standard of those on "Definetly Maybe". It probably didn't help that we were about a mile from the stage due to the huge crowd, and contributed to us concluding that, aside from a glorious rendition of "Slide Away", they "were much better last year."

When we'd booked our Glasto tickets back in March, The Stone Roses were billed to be the Saturday evening headliners but, thanks to John Squires cracked collarbone, they were unable to play. The music press had been buzzing with speculation as to who would replace the Roses. Rod Stewart, Madonna and Blur were all being mentioned. But, again showing that they were a family with the ability to turn festival water into wine, the Eavis's opted to give the coveted headline slot to Pulp, who had just had a huge hit with "Common People".

Everything about that warm June Saturday night was spot on. I was stood in this magical field with my two best mates, passing round a bottle of Southern Comfort, watching Jarvis stride onto the Pyramid Stage and rule Glastonbury. From old favourites in "Babies" to new songs such as "Sorted for E's and Wizz", (it was the supreme setting to debut that song) the ginormous crowd lapped them all up.

I loved The Stone Roses dearly and was gutted that they had pulled out, but they simply couldn't have put on as good a show as PULP did that night. After little over an hour of their sparkling performance, with band and crowd alike hot, sweaty and beaming huge smiles, Jarvis announced that the next song was to be the last.

Some songs are much better live than they are in their recorded format, they appear to get a new lease of life and this was particularly true for the epic final tune that night. As

Jarvis announced; "This is the last one, we can't do anymore. This is "....C....O....M....M....O....N....P....E....O....P....L....E", a lusty roar of joy went up from the crowd and we joined in with the other 60,000 folks pogoing, singing and hugging each other. It was an extra special moment, one of those that instantly seared itself into the area of my brain marked 'Recall if you need to cheer yourself up'. A memory that would still be in glorious technicolor and crystal clear 20 years hence when you are starting to struggle to remember simple life facts such as the names of your primary school teachers.

We spent the rest of the night buzzing our bits off wandering the site, laughing, drinking, taking legal highs that didn't alter your mood one bit, and then raving outside Joe Bananas Blanket Stall until 5am. As dawn broke over our campsite, with Jacko and Doody passed out in the entrance to our tent, I nicked Borg's last can of Fosters and took the long and winding walk down the hill to my spot at the front of the deserted Pyramid Stage.

I sat there and watched acid casualties stumble and fall to the ground, sleeping where they lay whilst late night courting couples ran back to their tents to get some fumbling in before the morning broke the spell that the night had cast over them. I pondered on the fact that my life was about to change. I was off to university in the autumn and sat there daydreaming about all the gigs I was going to attend, and all the books I was going to read. Coupled with the memory of the previous night's revelry I felt as contented and relaxed as I usually only did after eating a 12 inch cheese feast deep pan pizza. I began to let sleep envelop me as the sun was beginning to rise, safe in the knowledge that I was in my favourite place in the world. I was woken an hour or two later by a kindly litter picker who nudged me and said:

"C'mon mate, time to wake up. You must have been steaming when you fell asleep here, you've been laid in someone's Tofu stir-fry."

I thanked him and made my way back up the hill covered in the flavourless but pungent vegetarian meal. After a quick kip, we staggered out of our tents and, in traditional Sunday morning Glasto style, searched our rucksacks to see what provisions we had left. Our pool amounted to: A multipack of Mini-Cheddars, a Tracker bar and a bottle of Southern Comfort. That was breakfast sorted.

Unsurprisingly, I can't recall too much about that particular Glastonbury Sunday.

I went back to Hereford and, when not swimming or playing football, I would listen to 'Vauxhall & I' and ponder further on the changes that were about to crash into my life. Through the spring months I had kept in touch with Jess mainly by letter. She would send me long, floral outpourings detailing how much she missed me, I would reply with a single sheet explaining that I was very busy and quoting random Morrissey lyrics. Occasionally she would raise the romance killing spectre of me going to university in her letters but I just flatly ignored such talk. I still felt that I was committed to our relationship.

When my time at the school was over, I went home and spent any time we had together trying to fill her head with Morrisseyesque tales of difficult long distance romance being the best romance possible. I believed it all as well as I was totally swept up in Morrissey's love of unconventional relationships.

The 2nd big event of the summer of 1995 was mine and Jacko's long planned month-long inter railing trip. Thanks to my ever strengthening belief in "Braggism", I was desperate to go to the old communist bloc countries. Jacko was keen to visit Prague and Budapest, mainly because he had heard you could get a pint for the equivalent of 20p.

We planned our trip in extensive detail, well at least we thought we had. It was to be a month of adventure and exploration. Two childhood friends having a "Stand By Me" style trip before embarking on university life. In reality it ended up being 3 weeks (we ran out of money) of adventure, coupled with long train journeys, visa problems and me trying to explain to Slovakian waiters that vegetarians didn't eat bacon no matter how small the chef chopped it up. We returned to this Sceptred Isle a little wiser, with stories to tell (bribing a policeman to avoid prison in Romania was the best of them) and with a lot less money in our pocket.

Being back in Peterborough with only a couple of weeks left before my departure to Cardiff, I needed to get myself organised. This mainly involved having long, emotional conversations with Jess about the future. I was convinced that going to Cardiff wasn't going to change me. I was a fully formed adult who had held down a job, been to festivals, inter railing and, thanks to the teachings of Doody, knew how to handle my beer. What was university going to teach me about life? I was going there to read, learn and watch live music. As our relationship had survived the previous 4 months of long distance romance, I was convinced that it would survive me going away again. Jess was starting 6th form that September so we both had lots of studying to be getting on with. We made a decision that we would stay together and ring/write everyday to keep the romance alive.

I didn't really prepare for university life at all. I daydreamed a lot about it. I spent weeks deciding which CD's, books, posters of Morrissey, Orwell and Star Wars I was taking to put up in my halls of residence room. I bought tickets well in advance for Pulp and Black Grape gigs at my new student union and splashed out on what, on paper at least, looked like the dream ticket; David Bowie supported by Morrissey at the Cardiff International Arena. What I didn't think about was the impact that moving away from my family, friends and beloved football club would have. I had been to Hereford and convinced myself that going to university for 3 years was just the same as a 4 month stint teaching football to privileged kids.

As it turned out, my life was to change in a way that I hadn't foreseen at all. For the first time in my 19 years, I was about to fall in love.

Cardiff, Here We Come

ON a burning hot day in September, I said my goodbyes to my nearest and dearest. Stood on our driveway, I felt unusually devoid of emotions as Jess and Mum wept into their sleeves. It was no big deal. I was just going off to study and would be back home soon enough. I wasn't going to change. I was me and would remain so for better or worse. With our trusty Cavalier packed solid with my stuff, Dad drove me to Cardiff for the first time.

Upon arrival, we quickly located my halls of residence, which were called Talybont North (re-christened 'Talybronx' by the students). I unloaded all of my gear from the car into my room and said a neat, enemotional goodbye to Dad as he reminded me in time honoured style to ring Mum in the next hour;

Dad – 'You don't need to speak or anything, just go to the phone box, give her 3 rings and put the phone down. She will know that we got here safely, you're happy and I am on my way home.'

Me – 'Blimey, Mum should work for MI5 if she can deduce all that from 3 rings.'

Dad – 'Jeeez, Jay, you really need to work on your jokes if you are going to get a girlfriend whilst you're here.'

Me – 'I've already got a girlfriend Dad.'

Dad – chuckling – 'We'll see how that pans out son, we'll see.'

With that he gave me a huge hug, the likes of which he hadn't given me since England's World Cup semi-final defeat in 1990. As he let go and the air returned to my lungs, he said quietly:

'I'm very proud of you son. You are going to have a tremendous life and this place is going to be just right for you. You belong here, don't let anyone ever tell you that you don't, ok? Have fun, keep safe and remember that me and your mum love you.'

As I burst into a tsunami of tears and dived to hug him again, he turned away, already moving back to the safety of the car. The moment was fleeting and had now gone. As always, Dad had a peerless way to kill the emotion of the situation;

'You better wipe your eyes and stop crying. The lads in your flat will think you're a right nancy-boy crying because your dad's leaving. Go on, get inside and listen to your Morrissey tapes, and I will see you soon.'

With that he was gone and I ran to my room, shielding my tear-stained eyes in case anyone saw me and got to work rigging up my stereo. Within a couple of minutes I was blasting out "Your Arsenal" as loudly as the speakers could take. I was marking my territory.

The other 5 lads that shared my flat (no mixed sex flats in Talybont), were all sat in the kitchen chatting when I ventured out of my room. Over quick introductions, I found that they were all about to begin a Geology degree course and were all very much into their rugby. Months before we were assigned our rooms, I had filled in a questionnaire about my interests in order, I thought, to be placed in a flat with students that also loved Morrissey and Peterborough United. Looking around the kitchen, I concluded that my questionnaire must have got lost.

Despite their collective love of the oval ball, they all seemed decent enough and we spent that first afternoon sat around chatting about our lives and asking the standard university starter question, "What A-levels did you get?"

The only one of my new flatmates that really stood out was Matt. He arrived on his motorbike with the accompanying leather jacket, trousers and an openly Hells Angels attitude to women. His first words to me were;

'Alright mate, where are all the fucking birds eh? I thought this place would be full of fanny!'

My inner Braggism was just formulating a modern feminist response denouncing that sort of misogynistic rubbish when he slapped me heartily on the back, took the un-opened can of Fosters out of my hand and walked out of the room. He returned 10 minutes later draining the can and, upon seeing my proudly displayed PUFC badge, informed me that he liked football but didn't support a team. That instantly made me suspicious. Little did I know the impact that this grease-monkey was to have on my first few weeks in Cardiff.

My first meal at university was all set to be the traditional beans on toast. Unfortunately I had forgotten to bring a can opener, so decided to prise off the lid from the tin of beans with the sharp knife that Mum had insisted on me packing. As I plunged the blade downwards it took an angled bounce off the can and embedded itself into my left thumb. With blood squirting out of the gash, I refused all offers of help from my concerned flatmates and instead went to my room and used a whole roll of the sterilised bandage that Dad had liberated from the first aid box at his work. At this point, with my thumb pulsing in pain, I decided to give up on making tea and go to the Halls bar to get drunk.

First I had to pick which band t-shirt to wear for my first social interaction with my fellow students. Such items of

119

merchandise were a badge of honour, showing which clan I belonged to and where my allegiance lay. I pulled on my old faithful "The Queen Is Dead" shirt and made my way to the dark, bunker-like Talybont bar. I ordered a pint of lager and looked around, disturbed to see that, of the people in the room, one was wearing a Levellers long-sleeved top and the other two were sporting Welsh rugby shirts.

Due to a combination of nerves, fear and the fact that it was £1 a pint happy hour, I downed my first lager and greedily set about my second. Taking another furtive glance around the bar, I noticed a lad who, even sat down, looked about 8 foot tall and was sporting a Depeche Mode "Violator" t-shirt. Being from East Anglia, I wasn't used to being around tall people and I wasn't a fan of Depeche Mode but this was fast becoming a case of any port in a storm. I casually wandered over to this towering giant and gabbled an introduction in the standard new student manner, quickly listing: name, course, A-levels. Thankfully we were able to gain an instant insight into each other's music collection via the logos on our respective t-shirts. We quickly established our football fan credentials and that was it. Neil, the Depeche Mode and Spurs fan, was my first university mate.

After an hour talking music, football and a couple more pints, we plucked up the courage to ask the barman if it was always this quiet. Looking delighted at the chance to get rid of two of his tiny band of customers he gave us directions to the main Student Union bar that was a mile up the road. We trundled off in pursuit of our first big student night out, all the while keeping an eye out for any folks that looked like they might be suitable to join our newly formed indie music and football clan.

We made it to the union building and joined the snakelike queue, only to be quizzed by freaks and weirdo's about such varied subjects as: Star Trek, where to buy E's and whether the rugby lads drank in the Union bar? Those first few hours (and days) were like a gang recruitment drive. We had to make hasty, usually ilinformed decisions about whether someone was alright or not and whether we wanted to spend time drinking with them. We eventually got talking to two girls in the queue when we saved them from the clutches of Star Trek boy by pretending to be old friends of theirs. One of our new friends was a short, dark haired girl in a Manic Street Preachers t-shirt, who introduced herself as Louise in an accent that was unmistakably "propa cockney". My Grandad Bill had always advised me: "Never trust a cockney, they are always trying to sell you something or rip you off, the mouthy sods". So, despite Louise having the requisite band t-shirt, her cockneyness made me wary. My gaze then moved to her mate. I thought I was having a heart attack as she turned to face me and her exquisite mouth split into a show stopping smile. I had never experienced chest tightening pain when meeting a girl before and was beginning to scramble for breath and consciousness. She ignored my descent towards certain death and told me that her name was Amy. Even as the air mercifully made its way back into my lungs, I stood gormlessly staring at this vision of beauty with her English rose face, alabaster skin and dirty blonde bobbed hair. Thankfully Neil, seeing that my tongue had been stapled to the roof of my mouth, stepped in and introduced us. I was slowly regaining control of my functions as Amy looked at me with the kind of 'what the hell are you doing?' look that I imagine she usually reserved for close friends who decided to put their genitals in a clamp and then set fire to them. Both pity and disbelief were apparent in her voice as she said:

Amy: 'Errrr.... excuse me John, but you're dripping blood on my trainers.'

Me: 'What? Oh shit, sorry' as I looked down at my injured hand 'I cut my thumb opening a tin of beans with a knife earlier.'

Amy: "They were new trainers as well, Adidas Gazelles. I only got them yesterday.'

Me: 'I'm really sorry. I'm sure I've got a tissue here somewhere to clean it off.'

At this point, I reached into my jean pocket and pulled out a wad of blood encrusted kitchen roll. Amy looked at me with a mixture of disdain and a desire to never see me again and, without saying a word, turned away to talk to Louise. I'd blown it. Only I could fall for a girl and get her to hate me in less than a minute.

As Neil wet himself laughing at my entry for that years 'World's Worst Flirter' title, Louise and Amy reached the front of the queue and the bouncer ushered them into the SU Building. A couple of minutes later, Neil and I reached the stairway to student heaven and I attacked the bar the second we got through the door. After feeling the soothing chemical tang of lager in my throat, I calmed down a little and took in my surroundings. Although everyone we had met so far had called this place the SU Bar, it was set out like an old man's pub. It had low beams, dark corners, crap furniture and a ground in smell of fag smoke and disappointment. I had fallen for Amy and "The Tavern" all in the space of 10 minutes.

We found a table and I tried to put into words how I had lost the plot when meeting Amy. Neil just laughed and then laughed some more when recalling the fool I had made of myself in front of the first pretty girl I had met at university.

At 11pm, the last orders bell clanged and everyone in The Tavern made their way next door to the SU nightclub. I chuckled in quiet despair as we reached the front of the queue and were invited to hand over £1.50 to enter the "FUN FACTORY". As we walked through the doors, I could hear the first bars of Whigfields "Saturday Night" and felt like I had never left Peterborough. Neil found us some seats and I got the drinks in whilst scanning the crowd of fresh faced students, hoping to spot Amy.

As my fellow students drunkenly coupled off to begin their first regret filled university fumblings, Neil listened to my miserable complaining about it being: "Bloody awful in here" before spotting one of his flatmates across the dance floor and seizing his chance to get away from me. I found the darkest, dingiest corner and wondered if the feeling that was holding my stomach in a knot maybe wasn't about Amy or being in this club. I was homesick. I'd only been away from home for 15 hours but I missed it, suddenly felt very alone, far removed from everything and everyone that I loved. I thought about how much I missed Doody, Jacko and my folks so sat and planned my first trip back home to ensure that it coincided with a Posh home game. As I supped on my warm pint, I realised that I hadn't thought about Jess since I had waved goodbye to her that morning. In the days before I left for Cardiff, I'd had a nagging sense that it was time for me and Jess to split. We'd had some good fun but we were both heading out on completely different adventures. Of course, I didn't say any of this to her, I just constantly reiterated my "it will all be ok" mantra. Now, here I was not thinking about her and instead daydreaming about a girl whose trainers I had bled on a couple of hours previously.

Eventually Neil came back to find me and I told him that I needed to split up with my girlfriend. I had only known the poor lad for 3 hours but he summoned up his best advice for the occasion, "I'll get us another pint in then."

We spent the rest of that night propping up the bar talking football and music, watching the blur of student life fly around us. I was keeping one eye out for Amy but she didn't pop back into my life that night.

As we wandered home, I was full of giddy exuberance and fantasies about this beautiful girl whose trainers I had managed to ruin. I thought what a great story it would be to tell our kids about how we met. I was already planning that far ahead and was determined to find her again the next night and attempt to engage her in normal, non blood related, conversation. With this in mind, I made what ended up becoming a long-standing arrangement to meet Neil in our Halls Bar at 7pm the next night and went back to my flat.

Upon opening the front door, I was greeted by the noise of raucous dogs having sex in Matt's room. My flatmates, who were huddled in the corridor like naughty kids at a boarding school sneaking out for a midnight feast, informed me that Matt was in fact in his room with a girl. I just wanted to get to my stereo, to my new sanctuary and daydream about Amy. Over the next half an hour, the noise from Matt's room, which was 4 doors away from mine, got louder and louder. Even when my next door neighbour, Huw, shouted "Oi Matt, can you quieten it down a bit pal, I can't hear myself wank in here", the chuckles from my flatmates only masked the porn film soundtrack for a few seconds.

In order to get some sleep, I put Pulp "His 'N' Hers" on the stereo and held my headphones like a vice against my ears until I drifted off. I had some mad old dreams that night about pink glove wearing joyriders having babies. Just as I was dreaming that Jess's Dad was strangling me, I woke to find that the headphone lead had wrapped itself around my neck in the night. I glanced at the clock and seeing it was 8am thought that I might as well get up and find a shop that sold The Guardian and a local café that made a decent vegetarian breakfast. These were two important elements to my life and I needed to establish where I could find such things in this city as soon as possible.

As I was locking my door, I turned to see Matt opening his. Dressed in only his Mickey Mouse boxers and matching socks he looked down the corridor towards me and leered; 'Christ, that was some night, sorry if we kept you awake but some things just need to be done, know what I mean?'

I had no idea what he meant but smiled and said; 'Yeah mate, no problem.' As he moved aside to let his sex marathon partner out of the room, I caught a glimpse of a blonde bob as I finished locking my door. My heart realised who it was before my eyes did and went into spasm. As he slapped her now jean clad bum and lustily spat; 'Maybe see you again tonight luv for round 2?', my knees buckled and I had to hold onto the door handle to avoid sliding to the floor.

As he shut the door behind her, she and I exchanged an embarrassed "Hi", as the lyrics to Morrissey's "Oh Well I Never Learn" rumbled around my head. To avoid us both leaving the flat at the same time, I mumbled something about having forgotten a book and retreated. Safely inside my room, I put "Kill Uncle" into the 2nd hand Sony Discman that Jess had bought me as a leaving present, took a couple of deep breaths in an attempt to calm down before opening the door and striding quickly out of the flat. It takes a certain type of melancholic 19 year old to spend his first morning at university wandering the wet Cardiff streets and feeling a deep affinity with a song like "(I'm) The End Of The Family Line". I had only met Amy the previous evening but, in my dream world, I was already planning our first holiday together. I'd known that Matt was going to be a pain in the arse from the moment I met him.

After locating The Guardian and some perfect welsh rarebit, I perked up a bit and spent the rest of the morning wandering around the SU Fresher's Fair. By lunchtime I'd had enough of the forced fun on offer and walked back to Talybont. Through the haze of the previous night, I managed to recall which flat Neil was in and went to give him a buzz. It took me all of 5 seconds to persuade him that an afternoon in the pub was a good idea.

Once we'd sunk the first couple of pints, my inhibitions were just about loose enough for me to tell him about that morning's drama with Amy and Matt, much to his amusement. In a cloud of laughing, drinking and indie tunes on the jukebox, the afternoon morphed into the evening without us even realising. We watched new students come into this tiny bar, take one look at the ropey décor and us, before walking out again. We knew then we weren't going to be the bright new things of the 1995 Cardiff University intake.

At some point in the evening, Louise and Amy came into the bar and, seeing no better alternatives, decided to sit with us. My heart leapt when I saw Amy, which is never a good sign when a girl has just slept with one of your flatmates.

As the night descended into a blur of Southern Comfort, peanuts and storytelling, I discovered that Amy was apparently "very shy", could quite obviously handle her drink, liked the trip-hop scene that was achingly fashionable, that the only indie band that she liked was Suede and that she was from Cambridge. With her home city being only 40 miles from mine, she at least had heard of Peterborough. I even laughed along, whilst biting my tongue, as she told Louise (who had now instructed us to call her Lou) and Neil that it was a 'shithole'. I explained that due to the footballing rivalry between our two cities, I had a natural hatred of anyone from there. In a fit of giggles she, quite rightly, pointed out that 'Nobody cares about Cambridge United in Cambridge'. As she sat there laughing at me, not with me, whilst pushing her hair behind her left ear, I could feel myself falling for her.

She, on the other hand, couldn't wait to ask me "What do you know about Matt?" before proceeding to stamp on my feelings by telling me how amazing she thought he was. I should really have walked away at that point, wished her all the best with him and remembered that I had a girlfriend back home, or gone and thrown myself into the grinding mass of teenage sexual tension in our SU nightclub. Instead, I went to the bar and ordered another round of drinks.

The More You Sleep With Him, The Closer I Get

FOR the next couple of weeks, Amy, Lou, Neil and I would spend most evenings together in our Halls bar or The Tavern. Amy was undertaking an Archaeology degree course, which meant it was easy to come up with a nickname for her, and from then on I would regularly call her 'Indiana'. Oddly, she had wanted to take a couple of sociology modules so we found ourselves sat next to each other in plenty of lectures in that first term. Often we would leave the lecture and go and sit in The Tavern, gently wasting the afternoon away and talking about family, friends, music and the future.

One night I went (on my own) to a riotous Black Grape gig at the SU, complete with an off his tits Shaun Ryder falling off the stage. I arrived back in the Taylbont bar at just after 10.30pm and my gang all seemed pleased to see me, with Amy shuffling along in her seat to make a space. She asked about the gig and kindly wiped the sweat from my forehead that had gathered during my speed walk back to her. Just as I thought that we were getting close and her laughter meant that I should try and kiss her, Matt turned up. It was as if he had radar. As soon as last orders were called, Matt would miraculously turn up, out of nowhere, like the shopkeeper in Mr Benn. I would be stood at the bar getting the drinks in and would hear Amy shout over in her clipped Cambridge accent, "Jay, can you get Matt a pint of lager as well please?" I would slump at the bar, knowing that another night that had so much potential was about to be ruined.

I'm not sure if she realised that, as the days rolled past and we spent all this time together, I was falling in love with her. Matt certainly hadn't realised. He was just interested in his bike and getting Amy back to his room. In fact, in the year that I lived with him, I don't think I saw Matt show anything vaguely resembling an emotion. He wasn't the type. The only time I saw Matt express any feelings was during our second year in Cardiff, when we were part of the same football team that played a game against the university's Hellenic Society. It was a cup semi-final and a terribly violent game, with some of the worst tackling I had ever seen. After an hour of the game, the Hellenic centre forward didn't much like a sliding tackle I had made on him, got up from the puddle he had landed in, ran over and spat straight in my face. I wasnt a violent man and he was at least a foot taller than me but I lost the plot in that split second and spread his nose wide across his face with my forehead. Fair play to Matt, as the ref waved his red card in my direction and the baying hordes of Greeks bearing fists attempted to take my head off, he piled into the scrum and managed to keep me from certain death. When we eventually reached the relative safety of our dressing room, he told tell me that incident was his favourite moment of his time at university.

Back at the bar, Amy and Matt drank their last pint of the night, which I had paid for, then roared off back to our flat on his motorbike, leaving us mere mortals to trudge home in the rain. I went back to my room and again tried to block out the noise of her in his room by playing Pulp so loud through my headphones that my ears began to bleed.

Despite a new Morrissey album, 'Southpaw Grammar', having been released the month before I went to Cardiff, it was

"Viva Hate" that became the album that I turned to during this very odd period of my life. It's not that I didn't like "Southpaw Grammar', but that was an album for jumping around the room to. "Viva Hate" was an album to sit in the park to listen to and mope. Sleep was tough to come by knowing that the girl I had fallen in love with was in a room 10 yards away with another man. I sought solace with Morrissey in the form of "Everyday is Like Sunday" and the 7 minutes of sadness and humour that was "Late Night, Maudlin Street". I was confused, lonely and 200 miles away from everything I knew and loved other than this girl that had crash-landed into my life without her even seeming to notice. I clung to Morrissey like a life raft, desperately trying to find even more meaning in the words that he sang. He meant more to me in those first weeks in Cardiff than he'd ever done before. He kept me from running back home and giving up on Amy. I found a twisted sense of hope in songs like 'Alsatian Cousin' and knew that I had to hold on, tie my feelings up in a plastic bag and wait to see how this particular drama was going to play out. I was sure it wasn't going to work out in my favour and knew that Moz wasn't trying to signpost a potential victory, just that the song needed to play until its final note.

My inner Morrissey was telling me that I needed to put all of my emotional energy into this increasingly one sided romance with Amy. This in turn meant that I had to finally do the decent thing and split up with Jess.

I hadn't written to or telephoned Jess every day as I'd promised I would when I left dear old Peterborough in September. I had taken the cowards way out and hoped that in the 3 weeks I had been away from home she had got bored and decided that she didn't want a long distance relationship after all.

In mid October, I went home for Doody's 21st birthday and arranged to meet Jess on the afternoon of the party. It probably wasn't the greatest of ideas to agree to meet on "our bench" in "our park", as it maybe didn't give her a sense of what was about to come springing out of my mouth. She bounded into the park with a huge smile on her face and gave me an equally huge hug. I wasn't looking forward to what I was about to do. Startled by her affection filled welcome, I lost my nerve and bluntly blurted out: "I'm really sorry Jess but this long distance relationship isn't working. We need to split up now before either of us get hurt. It's not you, it's me....."

As the news hit her right between the eyes she started to cry. In that moment, I realised what an awful tosspot I had been to her and searched desperately for something to say that would stop her being so upset. As always, I reached inside my head for the file marked "Emergency Morrissey lyrics", and quoted some lines from The Smiths "I Started Something I Couldn't Finish...."

Mozzers wise words stopped Jess's tears as she went from crying to furious in the blink of an eye. She stood up from the bench, as did I, and she pushed me with both hands full in the chest. As I fell to the ground she stood over me and growled:

'You total and utter wanker, when are you ever going to grow up, Jay? You think quoting bloody Morrissey lyrics is ever going to help any situation? Ever? I really hope I never see you again.'

Still laid flat on the grass, I watched her walk away and thought that I'd deserved the push, the rant and if she had smacked me right between the eyes, I couldn't have complained.

That night I went to Doody's party at the local community centre, got drunk and talked rubbish with my oldest friends in the world. I was where I belonged, talking and joking with people that I loved. I decided that, despite Moz urging me to stay until the end of the song, I was going to quit university and move home. I would have my mates, some money (assuming I could get my old job back) and get to watch Posh every weekend. As long as I could afford a few CD's and go to a couple of gigs a month, what more did I need in the world? I went to bed happy in the absolute knowledge that I would never live anywhere other than Peterborough again. I had been away, tried it, hated it and so now was the time to head home and never leave. I wrote down my plan on the back of a McEwan's Export beer mat and stuffed it into my pocket for safe keeping.

When I woke the next morning though, she was back. With my mates at the party, I'd pushed all thoughts of Amy out of my mind, but in the cold light of morning, my infatuation was urging me to get dressed and run back to her. I laid back in my childhood bed and decided that now I was single, I would go back to Cardiff and tell Amy exactly how I felt, or, at the very least, make a drunken, piss-poor attempt at telling her. It would be my last stand, the epic squalling finale to the song. I had nothing to lose.

I got the painfully slow train back to Cardiff on the Sunday afternoon and spent the evening preparing myself for my big chat with Amy the next day. On the Monday after my 3pm lecture on Beveridge and the setting up of the welfare state, I felt a new found freedom and positivity. If this mesmerising vision of beauty didn't want to get with a young, newly single lad who had a head full of inspirational social policy and Morrissey lyrics, then more fool her.

I went to the bar at the now traditional time of 7pm. When Neil hadn't turned up by ten past, I went and threw pebbles at his bedroom window. He staggered to the window with what looked like a George Best sized hangover then, with a weary shake of the head, he redrew the curtains. I got back to the bar just in time to walk head first into Amy who was approaching from around the corner, causing my glasses to fly off and go skidding along the path. As she rubbed her head and swore under her breath, I scrambled to get my specs back onto my face.

Amy - 'Shit that hurts ... I was just running to meet you, I wondered if you would give up as nobody was here.'

Me - 'Running to meet me, that's a good start to the night. Usually you're running to meet Matt.'

As I silently scalded myself for saying such a stupid thing, I looked at the 'I'm hurt and offended' look that was spreading across her face and knew that I needed a plan, and quick. As per my training, under Doody's tutelage, I knew I had only option;

Me - 'Ignore me, I'm a twat. Let's get drunk, first round of Aftershocks are on me.'

Her mouth broke into the smile that had caused me to think I was having a heart attack when we first met and, within 5 minutes, the alcohol was easing the pain caused by our bumped heads and my irrational tongue syndrome. We talked, drank and giggled our way through the evening, just the two of us. I knew that Matt would arrive on the bell of last orders but I was determined to only worry about that when it happened. It was one of those nights where I was so totally engrossed in our conversation that I didn't notice that the rest of the bar had slowly filled with people. The kind of night where, in Hollywood rom-coms, we would be in sharp focus while the world flew around us in a blur. As the double Southern Comfort and lemonades eased my naturally occurring Englishness, I told her that I had split up with Jess.

Upon hearing this news, something odd happened with her eye, not so much a glint or a sparkle, more of a tic. She whispered an "Ok" whilst taking a hefty swig of her drink.

My brain had lost the radio signal to my heart with her simple, non-committal response. I had no idea what the right thing to say was, so wisely bit into my tongue until the pain caused it to spasm and didn't say anything audible.

After a minute or two of crippling silence, she pushed her fringe to one side and opened her eyes just enough for me to see a trace of a tear building before asking "I suspect I know the answer but why did you finish with her?"

I resisted the temptation to bring some humour to an ever darkening situation by saying 'Blimey you rate yourself, don't you?' Instead I let the alcohol, which was by now straining at its leash, take over my speech;

'Because of how I feel about you.'

She went deathly silent, looked into my raw, drunken eyes, leant over and kissed me full on the lips. As we locked in for the 2nd circling of tongues, somewhere deep down inside me, a feeling emerged that I hadn't experienced before. I knew then without a shadow of a doubt that I loved her.

We spent another couple of hours alternating between drinking and kissing before the dreaded bell for last orders rang and my focus switched to the bar doors, through which I was fully expecting Matt to walk any second. When he didn't come crashing in, I took it as a sign that it was now or never so turned to Amy and said; 'Do you fancy coming back to mine to listen to some music?' As we both burst out laughing and she chuckled, 'Sure, if that's all you want to do', I downed my drink and sprang to my feet, eager to get back to my room, to lock the door and keep the outside world outside.

It was only as we stumbled out of the bar arm in arm that it occurred to me that Matt might be in the flat when we got back there. When I opened the front door, I was relieved to see no sign of the motorbike warrior. I probably should have been more concerned when I noticed Amy sneaking a longing look at Matt's closed bedroom door. As it was, I just wanted to get us both into the safety of my room as quickly as possible. I relaxed as I locked the door behind me, lit some tea lights, put Portishead's debut album on the stereo before, in a twisted mass of band t-shirts, we tumbled onto the bed and spent the rest of the night wrapped up in each other.

I drifted off to sleep having taken dozens of mental photos of this beautiful girl who was already fast asleep across my chest. I needed to record our first time so I could recall the date in years to come, when we had friends over for dinner and they asked; 'So, when did you and Amy get together?'

I woke with a head full of cotton wool thanks to the Southern Comfort but with a smile on my face, only to find Amy frantically trying to find her socks in the dark;

Me - 'Are you ok?'

Amy - 'Shit, sorry I didn't mean to wake you.'

Totally misjudging the mood, I came up with a suggestion.

Me 'It's freezing, why don't you come back to bed and we can warm each other up?'

Amy: 'I've got a lot to do today, so I thought I'd make an early start.'

I steal a glance at my Indiana Jones alarm clock

Me: 'Errr, you do realise it's 5.30am?'

Amy: 'Yeah, but I don't want anyone to see me leaving....'

My heart sinks as I realise what she means. As she pulls on her Gazelles, still with a faint blood stain on the right one, she sits back on the bed, switches on the bedside Star Wars lamp and turns to me, her eyes set to full Bambi cuteness.

Amy: 'Jay, we're close right? I can trust you, yeah? Can you promise me one thing?

I know what she is going to make me promise and I also know that I am powerless to say anything other than;

Me: 'Yeah, sure.'

Amy: 'Promise me you won't tell Matt about last night, will you? It was lovely and all that but it was just a bit of fun, a drunken night. Just a student thing. You know how much I like Matt and I really want to see if we can get together properly. You understand, right? We're good, yeah? All sorted, yeah? You're such a good friend.'

With that she bent down, kissed my head and walked out of the room, having first opened the door slightly to make sure the coast was clear.

I lay there with my Peterborough United emblazoned duvet pulled up tightly over my face, hopes shattered, in sheets that smelt of her, trying not to cry. I had, I thought perfectly reasonably, been convinced that our kissing and her coming to my room was the start of something special. She had seen it as something quite different and was now desperate for Evel fuckin' Knievel not to find out. It was just a bit of fun for her, a quick exchange of bodily fluids between friends, no big deal.

The concept of casual sex hadn't really come into my life before, and certainly not with someone that I already felt so much for. Wasn't casual sex meant to be fun rather than invoking a feeling of gut shredding grief? In the same way that some people would reach for the bottle to ease the pain, I reached for the stereo. I knew that within my CD rack, I had the best medicine known to mankind. The sound of The Smiths filled my headphones. I played "Strangeways...." over and over again as the morning peaked its nosey beak through the thin curtains. I daydreamed about spending the short time I had left in Wales just listening to "I Won't Share You" on repeat.

Driven by hangover hunger, I eventually staggered out to the kitchen, only to encounter Matt, who was beaming like an idiot:

Matt: 'Blimey mate, sounded like a lively old night in your room. Anyone we know?'

A half second pause when I was tempted to tell him the truth before mumbling; 'No, just a girl from my course.'

Matt: 'Well, if you get bored with her, make sure you give her my number eh?'

At that point I gave up on food and retreated to my Smiths comfort blanket.

I wallowed in my room for most of the day reading Nick Hornby's "High Fidelity". I had read it so many times that the words had become as familiar and comforting as any Morrissey lyric. I wondered what my ex-girlfriends were up to, and made reams of Top 5 lists of everything from album covers to indie popsters haircuts just to stop me thinking about Amy. I cultivated a daydream about leaving university and heartbreak behind and opening my own 2nd hand music shop back home.

Through the late afternoon gloom, I remembered that I had a ticket to see Pulp play at our SU Great Hall that night. Thanks to the success of "Common People" and their triumphant Glasto appearance, this was the ticket that everyone wanted and, being the indie geek that I was, I'd booked my ticket months previously. Like the rest of the UK, Amy had fallen under Jarvis Cocker's spell so I had spent the last week trying desperately to get her a ticket for the gig, but so far without success. Instead, as I let the shower water finally wash the smell of her from my skin, I decided to use some of my closely guarded student grant money to buy her a t-shirt at the gig, in the hope that such an offering would help her fall in love with me.

I went to the Talybont bar earlier than normal, in the hope that the fizz of the lager could make dormant the volcano of pity that was threatening to engulf my innards. Of course, when I walked into the bar, Amy was the first person I saw. As I sat down with her and Lou, she acted as if nothing had happened. She was giggly from the Southern Comfort and slapped my arm when I said something funny, which had become an endearing habit and one that in my desperate mind told me that she did care after all.

I left them, halfway to steaming, at 7.30pm to walk to the SU, with strict instructions to ring the pay phone in the bar if I could get Amy a ticket from a tout.

As it turned out, the touts, who were always scousers no matter where in the country the gig was, wanted an extortionate £30 for a ticket with a £12.50 face value. Just to put that into context, £30 was the equivalent of my supermarket "big shop" for two weeks. I loved this girl, and she had made me lose control of my mind, but not my wallet. I went into the Great Hall on my own.

Pulp were on sparkling form that night and the crowd responded by jumping and dancing from the front to the back of the hall. Those were the very best gigs, where I removed myself from the real world for 90 minutes and revelled in the show this glorious band were putting on. I didn't think about Amy, I didn't think about missing home, I just got on with enjoying the tunes. This was the golden time to see Pulp, a band that were on the top of their game, flushed by their success but still playing in 800-1000 capacity venues.

With the final chords to "Common People" bouncing off the walls, I made my way out to the merchandise stall and handed over a sweat drenched £10 note in exchange for Amys new Pulp t-shirt. After a quick pint in The Tavern for rehydration and Dutch courage purposes, I made my way back to the Talybont Bar to present Amy with the token of my affection.

I got back to find Neil and Lou drinking Mad Dog 20:20 like it was water. In an attempt to set a Guinness World Record for the number of knackered livers in a single university, our SU had accepted Mad Dog's offer to sponsor the union that year. This meant that bottles of 20:20 were only £1 each in any of our bars. They were plastered but I managed to get out of them that they had no idea where Amy was. I figured that I should go back to my room, take a quick shower and change out of my saturated t-shirt and jeans, before coming back to the bar, where hopefully Amy would have turned up. I floated the 100 yards back to my flat daydreaming about the magical effect that the t-shirt would have on her.

As I turned the key in the front door of the flat, I was loudly whistling the tune to "Disco 2000", but the breath stuck firmly in my throat as I took my first step inside. There, in the doorway of Matt's flat was Amy. As she looked to the floor and darted into his room, Matt turned to me and said; 'Just off to bed now, mate', before letting out a rasping laugh, the likes of which I hadn't heard since Sid James got his grubby mitts on Barbara Windsor in the Carry On films.

I stood motionless, with my back pressed against the front door, trying to will my legs to move, to do something, to run before the noises began. The tears were rolling down my cheeks and I knew I probably had 30 seconds before one of my flatmates appeared in our communal corridor. I picked my heart and stomach up off the floor and staggered back to the bar to seek comfort with my mates.

As I approached the bar, I could see Neil's giant frame taking an unorthodox route back to his flat, like a drunk crab scuttling from left to right. When I went to open the bar door, Lou was stood in the doorway having a wrestling match with her jacket. She looked up at me and the twisted train wreck that was my face sobered her up in an instant; 'Oh Shit, after you went, Neil remembered that she'd left with Matt. Oh shit, shit, shit. Don't tell me that you have just gone back to your flat and seen them together?'

With a drunken hug and a misjudged pat on the cheek which ended up being a slap, Lou came up with a cunning plan; 'C'mon, let's go back to my flat, nick all the booze from peoples cupboards and get hammered, that'll help.'

I knew in that instant that I would forever be grateful to her for inviting me back to her room for a peach schnapps and a shoulder to cry on. She knew that I couldn't go back to my flat and listen to 'the noises', so I made a space on the floor and hunkered down in her old girl guides sleeping bag. The only problem with Lou's hospitality was her insistence that she could only fall asleep if the Manic Street Preachers "The Holy Bible" album was playing on the stereo. That was a tough album to listen to at the best of times, with its tales of self-abuse, anorexia and serial killers but, heartbroken and drunk, it was agonising listening. Waking up at 4am, sweating peach schnapps with the track "4st 7lbs" playing is a form of mental torture that I wouldn't have wished on my worst enemy.

I've Tried Really Hard
To Not Love You

WHEN I woke again at 7am, my first instinct was to go back to my room, stick "Vauxhall & I" on at full blast to wake the exhausted lovers, pack a bag and go home once and for all. I had tried to keep going until the end of the song but it couldn't carry on. Even Moz wouldn't want me to keep putting myself through this emotional torture, would he?

Whilst packing my rucksack, I remembered that my midday lecture was on Nye Bevan, so decided to attend one more session to say goodbye to university life before heading home. The last train out of Wales that would get me to Peterborough didn't leave until 6pm so I knew I had time to go to the lecture and have a few final pints in The Tavern before beginning the journey back to the bosom of my loved ones. I got to the cavernous lecture theatre early, took a seat on the back row and tried to stop my schnapps addled and sleep deprived brain from wondering whether Amy would turn up.

Just as the lecture began, she strolled in and, to my surprise, having looked around the room, bounded up the long staircase to sit next to me. Despite myself, my heart leapt as she sat down. I was dreading her not having had time to shower and smelling of "him", all cheap aftershave and engine oil. Thankfully, she smelt her usual flowery self. After she got her breath back, she reached across and wrote on my pad of paper:

"Sorry Jay, I didn't want to hurt you.   x"

Being the eternal indie geek, I scribbled:

"You've nicked that line from Teenage Fanclub's "The Concept".

She responded with a hastily scrawled:

"What, Teenage Fanclub have a lyric that says - Sorry Jay, I didn't want to hurt you?"

As we both burst out giggling and with the death stares of 200 students and 1 furious lecturer burning into our now bowed heads, I knew it would be ok. It would all work out between us one way or another.

After the lecture ended we walked arm in arm to The Tavern. Neither of us had mentioned going there, by now it was just the natural place for our legs to aim for. We stayed there for the rest of the afternoon having a battle of the jukebox. Her tune selections included Suede's "The Wild Ones" and for 4 minutes and 50 seconds of gorgeousness, we sat and listened, no laughing, no joking, no talking. I had fallen hard and, for the first time, I wondered briefly if she had as well. As I wobbled from my seat to select The Stone Roses 'I Wanna Be Adored' I caught her looking over at me and smiling, the kind of smile you can only display when you're drunk or are thinking; 'Hmmm, maybe I do fancy him after all'.

With Neil and Lou still recovering from their exploits with a MD 20:20 bottle the night before, the two of us eventually decided to head into town and found ourselves in Metros. It was a real old school indie night, £2 to get in, £1 a pint, carpet on the dance floor and The Smiths blasting out; it was a scuzzy shithole of a place that had fast become one of the highlights of Cardiff nightlife for us.

After an hour on the dancefloor producing our best shapes to the likes of The Cure and The Bluetones, we collapsed into a booth, sweatily chugging on bottles of Becks. I decided to take that moment to tackle the motorcycle shaped elephant in the room and told her that I knew she really liked Matt and that I wouldn't get in the way anymore and would just be her friend from hereon. She turned to me and shouted over the pounding beat to Pixies - 'Debaser':

'You deserve better than me.'

Me – 'The problem is, I don't want better than you... I want you.'

For a second she resembled a 30 year old woman looking back at her wasted teenage years spent with a worthless tosspot who eventually upped and left her, before saying:

'Oh you will Jay, trust me. One day you will want better than me, I know it.'

This girl talked in more rhymes and riddles than a Morrissey song so, without saying another word, I went to the bar, grabbed us another drink and dragged her back onto the dance floor as Happy Mondays 'Kinky Afro' blasted from the speaker stacks.

They finally threw us out of the club at 2am and we realised that we had to make the long walk home in the rain as we had pooled our resources to buy one last drink to share. I had suspended reality again and was living for the moment of sweaty joy that we found ourselves in. I gave up all ideas of leaving and went back to daydreaming about our first holiday together. When we got back to Talybont, it was a sodden hug and a lingering kiss on the cheek from her, then both back to our own rooms. I sat in the tiny en-suite shower in my room with the door open, 'Sproston Green' cranked up to 11 on the stereo, with the steam from the shower making the room resemble a scene from "Apocalypse Now" and allowed myself a little smile about the nights events. Huw hammering on the wall and howling; 'Shut the fuck up Jay, I've got a lecture in the soddin' morning', broke the spell somewhat.

The next two weeks were spent becoming engrossed in my course, missing home and falling ever more in love with Amy. We didn't kiss again or even go to Metros and now appeared to be officially wearing the 'just good friends' badge, especially when we would meet new people who would usually assume that we were a couple until Amy put them right. I even offered to use some of my student grant to buy her a ticket to see Morrissey support Bowie at the Cardiff International Arena. My thinking was that if I could get her into the same room as Moz, his magic would put a spell on her and she would fall deliriously into my arms. She politely declined my offer and so missed a very odd gig. Moz walked out onto the stage at 7.30pm to only a smattering of us devotees scrunched against the crash barriers. He was on towering form and smashed into the "Southpaw Grammar" material that made up the majority of the set with his normal violent abandon. The 200 of us pogoing and applauding wildly tried to create an atmosphere whilst the other 5000 people in the Arena looked bored or bemused. It was only as Moz left the stage that I realised what a humongous opportunity I had just wasted. The opportunity to get up onto the stage, with an ideal set of conditions; only a small set of Moz fans, a bored and uninterested set of security coupled with a low stage. The chance had gone and I would never get a better one to achieve the ultimate fan moment of scaling the stage and hugging him.

After that, Bowie seemed a terrible let down with a lumpen set of new songs and reworked inferior versions of the classics. It wasn't the man that had inspired me just 5 years previously, I knew he was the chameleon of rock but this was ridiculous, he wasn't meant to change from genius to dullard. By the time he was launching into his encore, I was already setting out on the 20 minute walk back to Talybont. Moz left the tour the next day.

I didn't see Amy in our flat again and didn't ask if Matt was going to hers now but, from what I could gather, all was not well between the two of them. I tried to stay out of it as much as I could and spent the time she and I were together trying not to look into her eyes or at her bum as she walked to the bar.

I never did find out exactly what went wrong between Amy and Matt but, one night in the depths of November, the pair of them had an ugly row, in front of an enthralled audience in the Talybont bar. Despite the rest of the room falling silent, I could only make out parts of the argument from 20 yards away. The words "arrogant wanker" and "dickhead" were screeched by her, with him responding with a rant about her being a "needy cow". Eventually, he stormed out of the bar and she came back to sit down with Neil, Lou and I, who, in a traditional English manner attempted to act like we hadn't seen or heard anything.

An hour and a medicinal double Southern Comfort after her argument with Matt, and with Lou and Neil at the bar, without any warning, as I was singing along to New Order's 'Temptation', Amy leant over the table and kissed me. Every molecule in my body wanted to kiss her back but even I had a modicum of self-worth remaining and pulled away. As she looked up at me with her big, confused eyes, I told her that I wasn't sitting in this bar kissing her an hour after her argument with Matt, that I was worth more than that. I then instantly shot down my new tough guy stance by reminding her that I loved her. I was on a roll now so told that if she wanted to be with me, for us to be a couple, she should kiss me again. She sat in her chair dissecting what I had said before gently whispering "Ok", then leaning over and kissing me again. My overriding emotion was one of relief. Moz had been right, I'd just had to hang in there and wait for her to realise that she wanted to be with me. The drama and heartbreak were over, we were a couple and would remain so forever, drinking Southern Comfort and listening to Suede. Of that I was certain.

We collapsed into her bed that night emotionally exhausted, I suspected for very different reasons. I woke at 7am to find her hugging me very tightly, in the same way a boa constrictor holds its prey. I had the joy of a 9am lecture on the Russian revolution so had to get up and out of her room but, between the kissing and at least one more return to under the duvet, we made a plan to meet in town at midday for "something to eat". This was getting refined, we had never been to a restaurant together before. It was bloody tough to leave the bed of the girl I loved to go and learn more about Lenin but I was determined to be seen to play it cool. I didn't intend to get anywhere near the misogynistic wanker style that Matt had perfected but I also knew that I needed to be an equal partner in this blossoming romance.

At 12.03pm I sprinted from Spillers Records (where I had been stocking up on more obscure and unwanted indie CD's for £1 each) to Bella Pasta. Thanks to the constant Cardiff rain my jeans felt like they weighed a ton and with hair stuck to my forehead and glasses, I looked like I'd taken up competitive crying. I was almost overcome with emotion as I crashed through the doors to see this beautiful woman quietly chuckling at my bedraggled appearance. Over our shared starter of garlic bread (with cheese), we chatted and laughed as normal, though this time over a bottle of house white wine. When she ordered the wine, my first thought was; "I've only got £10 in my pocket thanks to my CD buying so I hope this is her treat."

After 3/4 of the bottle had been sunk and my fringe had begun to dry, Amy went very quiet and bowed her head ever so slightly. A wave of panic washed over me as I thought the song was about to end in a way that Moz would love, with her announcing that last night had been another drunken mistake. Instead she took an audible deep breath and blurted out:

'I love you, Jay. There I said it. I've tried really hard to not love you. I didn't come to university to fall in love with anyone and, no offence, but certainly not with a Morrissey obsessive who would rather spend all his money on CD's by bands nobody has ever heard of rather than pay for a decent bottle of wine. I came to enjoy student life, to go to cool clubs and see how different life could be, see where it could take me. Instead I fell in love with you. I know you Jay, I know all you want from life right now is your music, your football and me, but I want so much more. But anyway, as I said, there is no point denying it anymore, I am totally and utterly in love with you.'

As declarations of love go, it wasn't exactly up there with "Breakfast At Tiffany's" or even Leia and Han in "Empire Strikes Back". In fact, it had a distinct ring of Morrissey about it.

I sat there with an inane grin on my face as we finished our penne pasta and Amy paid the bill. I used my tenner to treat us to a cab back to Talybont where we ran up the stairs to her 6th floor flat, crashed through the front door and spent the next 3 days and nights locked in her room. We were in a frenzied race to find out as much as we could about each other before the real world forced its way back into our lives. The only time I left the room was to pop out and get essential supplies (pizza, beer and CD's).

This was us now, we were a couple. She had written "Amy Loves Jay" on a piece of scrap paper and I would carry it round with me like an ID card, ready to show it to anyone that asked where I had been or what I was up to. With that feeling of desperation to know everything there is to know about the other, it was amazing how intimate we became in such a short space of time, from sharing tales of our childhood through to attempting to re-enact the More Magazine "Position of the Fortnight". Try as we might, any position with a difficulty rating of 4 or over was just impossible for anyone but a pair of Olympic gymnasts.

By the morning of our 4th day spent locked away from the world, I had no choice but to drag myself away from my new love and head back east to see two of my everlasting loves, namely my mates and The Stone Roses. Doody, Jacko and I had got tickets to see The 'Roses, first in Leicester where Jacko was at university, then onto Norwich for the second night where we would stay with our old mate Mark and go to the UEA hall to see our heroes perform. It was a lads weekend that I had been looking forward to for months but leaving Amy's bed was tough. We exchanged Portishead & Morrissey t-shirts in the same way that footballers swap shirts at the end of a momentous game, knowing that wearing the others clothes would keep a piece of them close during our enforced break. Her skinny fit t-shirt was a little snug over my lager enhanced stomach but I wore it with the pride of a 19 year old man in love. Well, I did until my mates saw it and took the piss so much that I took it off.

None of us had seen The 'Roses before and my adrenaline levels would have enabled me to run from South Wales to the Midlands. Here I was, off to see one of the greatest bands in the history of pop music with my best mates in the world, knowing that back in Wales, the girl I loved was waiting for me.

Standing in the middle of the De Montfort Hall and watching this almost mythical band walk out and play "I Wanna Be Adored", "She Bangs The Drums" and "Waterfall" as their first three songs was almost beyond my comprehension. I lost myself that night, dancing like a fool with my face fixed in a permanent Bez style grin. I know deep down that it wouldn't have been that good, as both John Squire and Reni had been replaced by session musicians by that time, but for me to see a band called The Stone Roses play those songs was more than enough.

They were just as sublime 3 days later at the UEA in Norwich. Unbelievably, in a venue that held maybe 1000 people, you could walk up and buy a ticket to the gig the morning before they played. We danced, we hugged and further reinforced friendships that we knew would last forever.

The next morning, I was up and out of Mark's flat as soon as my hangover allowed my legs to move in a vaguely straight line. With Doody and Jacko gently abusing me for, 'Running back to your Mrs', I gave them both a final, 'You're just jealous boys, enjoy the journey home' and was out of the door. The train journey from Norwich to Cardiff was a tortuous 6 hour slog but I couldn't wait to get back to her and found myself pacing up and down the length of the train, willing it to speed up and deliver me back to her bed. When not pacing, I spent the journey gazing out of the window. daydreaming that I was one of those men in a country song, riding the rails back to my girl. Our love affair resumed with a pint and a slobbery kiss in the Halls Bar, and we spent the weeks leading up to the Christmas break exploring each other's bodies, minds and music collections. She even managed to persuade me to hire a tuxedo and buy tickets to the SU Christmas Ball. I lasted an hour, most of which was spent moaning about 'looking like a div', before we went back to hers, got changed and went to the pub. Amy was learning fast that it wasn't going to be easy being in a relationship with me.

Despite now being very much in love, we were also both desperately homesick. In Amy's case, she would literally be sick thinking about how much she missed home. I would stand and hold her hair back as she dry heaved while recalling memories of her family and friends. We built up a mythology about how stupendous our home cities were and would unintentionally torture ourselves by recounting tales of home to each other. In fairness to Amy, where she lived, in a little picture postcard village just outside Cambridge was well worth being homesick for. It was a beautiful place where, that Christmas in the snow, we walked her dog through endless fields before going back to her parents' house for hot chocolate in front of the open fire. Come the evening, her mum would present a glorious home cooked meal and her dad cracked open the Adnams ale. Despite her parents not wanting us to sleep in the same room, I would sneak in after lights out and only go back to the spare room when her dad popped downstairs in the morning to make everyone a cup of tea. It had been the perfect Christmas and she was understandably considering not leaving this idyll to go back to university.

I would have quit Cardiff as well if she had. I had a burning desire to go home but knew that I could only do that if Amy came with me. She was more important than my education and I would have gone anywhere she wanted if it meant us being together. Many a time over that Christmas break, I asked her if we could quit university to go and get jobs and a house in Peterborough. She would give me her best sarcastic smile and simply say;

'I don't love you that much, Jay.'

As the holiday period came to an end, despite her homesickness, Amy decided to head back to Cardiff. I went too.

1996

Pubs, Gigs & More Magazine

AS it now appeared that we were both staying in South Wales for the long haul, I was determined to get on with student life. I had spent the first term lusting after Amy and missing home but this term was going to be different. I was, for the first time in years, genuinely content with my life, other than the bone-gnawing homesickness. I had a very simple test to ascertain my level of happiness. I would put "Unlovable" by The Smiths on the stereo and, If I smiled at Mozzers lyrics, then all was well in my world. Listening to the song and pulling the duvet over my head to shut out the world was a sign that I wasn't in a good place. We would spend every possible hour together, most of them spent talking, drinking or entwined and Amy seemed as intensely happy as I was. I knew that there were things about me she wanted to change, but she'd realised that I was a stubborn, Morrissey obsessed football fan and that although they could be very boring character flaws at times, she loved me nonetheless. I did have a lot of annoying traits, not least of which was the fact that I was a terrible inverted snob. I saw myself as some kind of working class hero battling against the upper-middle class students who were everywhere I looked. The type of students whose parents gave them more a week in "spends" than I had earned working a 40 hour week back home. The angry working class boy from Peterborough was never far from the surface, ready to have an argument on any subject. I was a fully-fledged follower of the Billy Bragg political ideology and was immersed in my Social Policy degree.

I hadn't visited Cardiff before that first day at Talybont, I didn't feel the need to. I read the prospectus that had details of the gig venues and a photo of Nye Bevan statue standing proudly in the city centre. I was hooked just by those two things. I had read so much before even beginning my degree about Bevan and his role in creating the NHS and was desperate to learn more and to see his statue on a regular basis.

One Tuesday night, Amy and I were wandering through the almost deserted streets of the city centre when I spotted some rugby lads hoisting the smallest member of their group up onto Nye's statue. When he had scrambled to his feet, he placed a traffic cone on old Nye's head, much to the delight of his knuckle dragging mates. I wasn't having that so, after the group of cultural vandals had moved away, I decided to climb up the statue and take down the offending item. Amy cheered her encouragement as I made my way up. I eventually reached the top and ripped off the cone, restoring Nye to his former glory. Unfortunately, the removing of the cone put me fatally off balance and I tumbled through the air with all the grace of Eddie 'The Eagle' Edwards and landed, knees first, onto the pavement. As I examined my ripped jeans and shredded hands, Amy surveyed the potentially pathetic scene, selected her best weary smile and said:

"You know what Jay, I think you care more for that bloody statue and Morrissey, than you do for any human being."

Amy and I spent the first few months of 1996 in a blur of pubs, gigs and running back to her flat to lock the door after buying that week's copy of More. We had contracted that desperately in love virus where every second apart felt like a temporary break up and powered up our hormones for the next encounter. One afternoon we got onto the scales and found we had both lost over half a stone in a week. We had simply forgotten to eat. We'd had more important things to do. Neither of us travelled home that term, as much as we missed it, we were so important to each other that the thought of spending a weekend apart was horrifying.

In the Easter holidays, I took Amy back to Peterborough for the first time. She was her usual fragrant, ultra polite self when meeting my parents, who instantly fell for her. She was, though, very nervous about meeting my mates. The two of us stood outside my local pub, The Swiss Cottage, as she gripped my hand and asked; 'What's this pub like, Jay?'

Me: 'It's my local, I've been drinking in here since I was 16 with Doody and Jacko. It's tiny inside, about the size of a living room but everyone knows each other so it's fine.'

My description didn't help her nerves.

As we walked through the pub door, Doody gave his usual greeting to anyone he met for the first time; 'Nice to meet you, what are you drinking?' and she began to feel at ease. This particular night was Maundy Thursday which, with the lure of a bank holiday the next day, was always a big night out. After a few drinks in The Swiss we got a cab into town and I was persuaded by the boys and an intrigued Amy to join the queue to get into 5th Avenue. Once inside the neon lit nightclub, Amy turned to me and said 'This is superb, an 80's themed 'club!'. I didn't have the heart to tell her that the club wasn't trying to be kitsch or retro, this was it trying to be hip in 1996. Due to the sheer number of people out on such a night, you were always guaranteed to bump into old school mates and ex-girlfriends. Jo was first up and, having seemingly drank her own bodyweight in Hooch, she wandered over with her boyfriend to make formal and stilted introductions;

Ignoring me and looking Amy up and down.

'I'm Jo. I went out with Jay for ages. Good luck with ever

getting him to smile or enjoy life. He's a right miserable sod; I am sooooooo much better off without him.'

Amy: 'Didn't you split up years ago?'

Jo: 'Yeah, almost exactly 4 years ago.'

Amy: 'Well I'm pleased you've moved on. Now, will you excuse us, my boyfriend is desperate to go and dance to this song, it's his favourite.'(Gina G - 'Ooh Aah... Just A Little Bit' was the song in question).

With that, she linked her arm through mine and led me giggling, not to the dance floor but to the upstairs bar for a much needed drink.

With the night drawing to a close, the DJ put on Oasis 'Don't Look Back in Anger', which seemed a bizarre choice for the 'Erection Section' but it saw me drag my girlfriend onto the dance floor. As I spun her around, whilst mouthing the words to the song to each other in an exaggerated half-cut manner, we bumped into a blonde haired woman who appeared to be having her face gnawed off by her dancing partner.

Me: 'Oooops sorry m'duck, an accident that..... Alright Kate, how ya doin?' (as always when drunk and back home, my Peterborian twang was back in full effect)

Kate: 'Errr...yeah watcha.'

With Noel in full flow, singing about Sally's need to wait, Kate steals a quick look at Amy and shouts into my ear.

Kate: 'She looks nice, too good for you! I'd heard you'd finally found your 'true love'. Good luck with it, maybe she'll enjoy the note filled with Morrissey lyrics when you get bored and leave her.... Right, well, good to see you but we'd better be heading off.'

She takes the hand of the fella she was dancing with and goes to lead him off the dance floor. As she does, this lad, who

I have never seen before, turns to me and snarls:

'Just piss off and leave her alone mate. She's mine now, you missed your chance.'

Rather than get into a pointless row about him not being my mate, that Kate and I had split up in 1994, and that I was deliriously happy with my girlfriend thanks very much, I just smiled at him. He wasn't sure what to do with that, so flicked me the middle finger as a red-faced Kate dragged him away.

I turned to find Amy in hysterics as Noel was telling us to not look back in anger one last time. We walked back to the bar and, as I was ordering the ridiculously watered down drinks, she recovered her powers of speech and said:

'I take it that was another one of your ex-girlfriends? Not exactly queuing up to form a fan club are they? This city is fully of nutters and that has made my night. Right come on I've had enough of this place, I want a kebab. As you've been abused by two of your ex-girlfriends, I'll even treat you to a veggie burger'.

I bloody loved that girl.

When we returned to Cardiff it was time to plan where we were going to live during the next academic year. Over a cup of disgusting fruit tea in the kitchen of Amy and Lou's flat, we agreed that the 3 of us and Neil would live together as a dysfunctional family. By virtue of losing a game of rock, paper, scissors, it was decreed that I would be responsible for finding our new home. I figured that I had a few weeks to get organised and find a place so continued to spend my time in Amys bed, in a lecture theatre or The Tavern. What I hadn't realised was that the day the 'housing list' of approved landlords was released my fellow students were all out snapping up the best houses. By the time I ambled in to collect the list from the Accommodation Office it had barely 10 properties left on it.

For weeks Amy had been hearing from her coursemates

about the great places they had arranged to move into. She kept reiterating that she trusted me to 'find us somewhere amazing' and it was those words that looped round inside my head as I began to investigate the properties on the list. After looking at 3 houses where I half expected David Frost to meet me at the door to ask 'Who would live in a rancid flea-pit like this?' I retired to the pub. After a couple of pints I went to the next address on my list, 28 Wyverne Road. The lad who opened the door looked like every ounce of blood had been drained from his emaciated body, which is never a look that estate agents recommend when showing people around. He explained that him and his mates were final year Law students and had; 'Gone a bit mad in this house mate I'm afraid. Once we realised it was a crap hole we abused it. We've ruined the sofa, the carpets and the bathroom. The boiler only works when you don't want it to and we lock the front door by tying loads of elastic bands around where the lock used to be. The rent's really cheap though.' Despite his withering assessment, I didn't want to look at any more houses, I wanted to go back to the pub. I reckoned on being able to talk the landlord into doing the place up a bit before we moved in and the downstairs room I wanted was the least disgusting in the house. Plus it was very cheap.

I went back to the Accommodation Office and told them that we would take the house. Maybe when they asked, 'Are you sure? You've been to visit the house, yeah? The house with the elastic bands on the door?' I should have thought again but I wanted to go back to the pub to see my girlfriend and tell her that I, her hunter-gatherer, had sorted us some top quality accommodation. Amy was delighted at my description of the house, mainly because I didn't describe 28 Wyverne Road. Lou and Neil even insisted on buying me a few drinks and taking me out for a pizza to thank me for finding such a first class house. I put their inevitable disappointment to the back of my mind and ordered a thin crust Fiorentina with no olives.

We finished our first year at university in a blaze of sunshine and afternoons in pub beer gardens. None of us really wanted the summer to usher us back to our home cities and that alone was a huge change for Amy and I. We made plans to see each other every weekend, mainly by me travelling to Cambridge. Everything felt right with the world.

This Gig Is Way Too Big

THE first half of 1996 had been an indie music wasteland, still dominated by the release of Oasis' "(What's The Story) Morning Glory" the previous year. That was an album that had me firmly under its spell from the opening guitar strum of 'Hello'. It wasn't as raw as "Definitely Maybe", but it was full of anthemic hits and as us indie kids weren't used to such things, it felt new and exciting. 'Wonderwall' and 'Don't Look Back in Anger' went on to rule the world but, for me, "Cast No Shadow" was the moment of pure genius.

They had also entered into the chart war with Blur the previous summer. I had no problem with two of the truly stupendous indie bands launching singles in the same week as each other but did they really have to release their worst songs as singles? "Roll With It" (Oasis) and in particular the charmless witticisms of "Country House" (Blur) were my absolute low point of Britpop. "Roll With It" was easily the most lumpen and ordinary of "Morning Glory's" tracks and "Country House" was Albarn showing that he was fast disappearing up his own arse in a cloud of cockernee (sic) laddish banality. Or maybe he was trying to be ironic? I didn't care, the song was crap. It was a 'war' that created headlines on 'News At 10', saw hundreds of thousands of singles sold and saw ordinary folks telling anyone willing to listen whether they were 'Oasis' or 'Blur'. I bought both singles even though I didn't like the songs, as the geek in me needed to own the B-sides.

With no Glastonbury in 1996, all roads led to Knebworth Park in August where Oasis were due to play to over 250,000 people across 2 nights. The papers reported that 1 in 10 households in the UK applied for tickets for those gigs. That was a mind-blowing rise for a band that only, 2 years previous had been under Chumbuwamba on the Glastonbury bill. I got tickets for Amy and I, by standing outside Cardiff International Arena from 4am until the box office opened at 9am on the day tickets went on sale, and I wasn't even the first in the queue. The gig was months away, and thousands of sad gits like me were standing outside venues (that had been designated 'Oasis Box Offices') up and down the country, in order to secure tickets. For the weeks leading up to the gigs, the buzz around them was inescapable. I couldn't go to a pub, football match or gig in either Cardiff or Peterborough without someone asking; 'Are you going to Knebworth?"

When we arrived at Knebworth, that Saturday lunchtime, I began to get a sense of how big this thing was when the coach park stretched as far as the eye could see. I had been to big gigs and festivals though, I knew the score. I hadn't though considered the enormity of 125,000 people standing in a field. As we handed over our tickets at the turnstile, Amy and I looked in awe at the sheer overwhelming size of the place. We found a decent spot only about half a mile from the stage and sat down to watch the support acts, who did their best to fill this vast open air arena. Not all of them succeeded, with the Chemical Brothers banging dance beats and light show falling a little flat at on a blazing hot summer day in a field the size of Newcastle. The Manic Street Preachers instilled some atmosphere into the day later on with their shouting and rock anthems, before The Prodigy came on and rattled the grass to its roots with a teeth-shaking techno-pop romp.

Oasis sauntered onto the stage in front of the adoring hordes as the sun began to set, and did what they did best by playing huge rock 'n' roll songs. It was a glorious hour spent dancing and hugging the girl I loved, watching the biggest band in the world do their stuff, and singing songs like 'Acquiesce' to each other before collapsing in a fit of giggles. This was a moment in time, a band that were on the crest of a wave, and maybe, just maybe, went over the top of the wave and "jumped the shark" that very night. As Noel stood back from the microphone, abandoning his attempt to sing the monster hit single that was "Don't Look Back in Anger", to a mass singalong, I noticed, to my right, that a huge brawl had broken out. I'd never seen anything like that at a gig before and I got a bit nervous after that as the fight got ever bigger and closer to us.

I don't blame the band but the facilities that day at Knebworth were bloody awful. It was well over an hour long queue to get a pint or a pie and the queue for the toilet was even longer. Amy had the patience of a saint, as I moaned and groaned my way through the queues. Aside from the bands and Amy's sparkling company, I moaned about almost everything that day and although it wasn't the last day out with Amy that I came close to ruining, it was certainly the first.

My moaning was compounded by having my first ever panic attack when attempting to leave the field in the dark after Oasis had finished. These hordes of people that had seemed a thing of wonder earlier in the day, now appeared to resemble an army marching to the frontline in the darkness. With my palms beginning to sweat and my heart racing, I knew that I needed to get back to the safety of our coach as quickly as possible. Unfortunately, the vast temporary coach park didn't have any lighting set up and, suddenly, all the hundreds, if not thousands, of coaches all looked the same. In my frenzied state, I took the easy option. I blamed Amy:

"How can you not remember where our soddin' coach is, or even what it looks like? Do I have to do EVERYTHING? You're meant to be the intelligent one in this relationship for Christ sake, can't you remember anything?"

My twisted, panicked brain was ignoring two very obvious facts:

1 – They didn't teach "finding your coach in the dark" on Amy's Archaeology course.

2 – Why couldn't I remember where the coach was?

Thankfully Amy ignored my ranting, locked me in a bear hug and gently talked me down, like a concerned cat owner coaxing their errant moggy down from a tall tree. In a twisted mass of tears, snot and arms we eventually stumbled. We found our seats and settled in for the inevitable delays that we would face in returning to the real world. With my beautiful, kind girlfriend stroking my hair, I put my head on her shoulder and fell soundly asleep until we got home.

1996 was, despite the general music malaise, an exceptional time to be an indie music obsessive and living in Cardiff. It felt like the musical hub of the whole world for a few months and we threw ourselves headlong into it. You couldn't walk around the city centre without wandering into a Super Furry Animal or go to a pub without seeing Cerys from Catatonia having a pint and holding court, surrounded by devotees.

The Super Furry Animals had first scorched into my life when they supported a band whose name I'd forgotten before they'd finished their set, at our SU club. After ambling onto the stage, this ragged, hairy mess of Welshmen blasted out 20 minutes of space-rock for the small gaggle of hardcore indie types that always made a point of watching the support bands. Their debut single "Hometown Unicorn" was a spectacular statement of intent. It's chorus talk of going back to your hometown, struck a chord. One of us would put it on the jukebox in The Tavern for Amy, Lou, Neil and I to scream along, letting loose the feelings of homesickness that we fought to keep locked in our respective cages.

The other place we would hear that tune was at the superb

Clwb Ifor Bach. The club was located smack bang in Cardiff city centre and, on a Wednesday night, hosted 'Popscene', the only club night at which students and locals would happily mix. It had dance music on the bottom floor and a middle floor that was full of sofas, games consoles and chill out tunes. The top floor was our home from home. A space where they combined an indie disco with the very best new bands that Wales and England had to offer playing live sets. That small, dark, top floor space was a slice of heaven and one of the very few places in which I felt comfortable as soon as I walked through the doors.

I would go and watch SFA, or any of the other emerging Welsh bands whenever they played in Cardiff or nearby in the likes of Newport or Swansea. Amy would get stressed about me going to gigs on my own, she saw it as further confirmation that I didn't ever want to make new friends. I would get back from a solo gig, go up to her room to say goodnight and she would quiz me about any potential friends;

Amy - 'Did you see anyone you knew?'

Me - 'Yeah a couple of people from my course were there, and that weird couple who only speak Welsh from yours.'

Amy - 'Did you speak to any of them?'

Me - 'Does a nod count?'

Amy - (giggling) 'Oh Jay, what are you like? Did you speak to anyone tonight between saying 'bye to me and coming back here?'

Me - 'Of course I bloody did.'

Amy - 'Ordering a pint from the barman doesn't count!'

Me - 'Well in that case, no I didn't speak to anyone.'

Amy - 'Please don't trot out your, "I don't need any new friends, I've got Doody and Jacko" line again. I know they are your best mates and you would 'walk in front of a double decker

163

bus for them', but I'm sure they wouldn't get offended if you made some new friends.'

Me - 'Lou and Neil, you even, could be classed as new mates.....'

Amy - 'So that's it? You're going to spend 3 years surrounded by 30,000 other students and you are only going to speak to us 3. I love you Jay but you're mental.'

With that she gave me a hug and I filed that conversation away with all the others we'd had about making new friends.

As well as SFA, the other big Welsh prospects that autumn were Stereophonics. I knew that they were going to be big from the first time I saw them. That wasn't me trying to be smart, anyone with functioning ears worked it out within 5 minutes of hearing them. In fairness, I did think that a lot of bands from that South Wales scene were going to be huge. After the release of their debut album 'The Big 3', I spent weeks telling anyone within earshot that 60 Foot Dolls were going to be bigger than Oasis. We first saw Stereophonics supporting a band in our SU club. I was so blown away by their set that I didn't even hang around to watch the main act. The band were manning their own merchandise stall and I sauntered over to get my hands on their limited edition debut CD single "Looks Like Chaplin/More Life In A Tramps Vest". I bought 3 copies and the bands handsome lead singer asked me "Why 3 copies mate?" I told him that I would play one and keep the other 2 in pristine condition as one day I would make a good few quid by selling them. He couldn't stop laughing and shaking his head as he signed all 3 copies, and we wished each other well with our endeavours.

Aside from Oasis at Knebworth, the summer was dominated by the Euro '96 football tournament, which ended in yet more heroic failure for England. I managed not to cry, unlike in 1990, when England again lost on penalties to the Germans in the semi-finals, so I figured that I was maturing. It was the first summer football tournament where Doody, Jacko and I were old enough to be out in the pubs of Peterborough watching the England games. When Gazza scored that goal against Scotland the whole of the Whittle Way in Stanground exploded in celebration. Unfortunately, after the Germany defeat, many of my fellow football fans lost their minds. We had watched the game in the 'Posh Pub' situated in the main stand of the Posh ground and on our way out, found the doorway blocked by a lad in a yellow Diadora shell suit, with a Union Jack draped over his shoulders.

Him - 'You pair of queers German or what?'

Jacko and I (in unison) - 'You what mate?'

Him 'You both got Adidas trainers on ain't ya? They're what Germans wear and we only want English in here. You wanna fuckin' start do ya?'

As he drunkenly lurched towards us, I resisted the temptation to point out that he was wearing a track suit made by an Italian company and a flag that was celebrating the United Kingdom rather than simply dear old England. Thankfully, as he got to within a couple of feet of us, Doody, who had long been our 6 foot tall guardian angel arrived on the scene.

Doody - 'You've got two seconds to do one , or I am going to knock you down those stairs...it's up to you?'

The Italian/British ruffian took one look at Doody and decided the game was up. He wouldn't get the chance to give two 'Germans' a good hiding after all.

I spent the summer working at Pearl and going to see Amy in Cambridge every weekend. With no Glastonbury on offer, we decided instead to get weekend tickets to the inaugural V Festival at Chelmsford. It looked like a star-packed festival with Pulp and Weller headlining and the likes of The Charlatans, SFA and Supergrass also on the bill. All of those acts played their part in making it a cracking weekend as the two of us cackled and drank our way around our first festival together. The difficult, mesmerising and emotional moment for a dedicated Charlatans fan such as I came when the band took to the stage mere weeks after the loss of their Hammond organ alchemist, Rob Collins. I cried like a big girl when I first heard the news about Rob's car accident, and the tears flowed again in that Chelmsford park as the band battled bravely on with the show.

The festival itself felt sanitised, corporate and safe. The safety element was ok, as I quite enjoyed not having that constant fear of rampaging gangs of lads robbing tents that we had at Glastonbury. The corporate feel and the strict rules about where you could camp, what you could do and where, were frustrating. On the coach back to Cambridge, I told Amy that I was glad we had gone as that would be the first and last V Festival, that nobody would put up with that kind of regime again.

Squashed Slugs & Smashed CD Cases

IN early September we returned to Cardiff and into our own house. No more Halls of Residence living, we were now adults all set to organise our own TV licence and gas bills. Unfortunately, the house that I had signed us up for was an old decrepit wreck with damp, slugs and the coldest bathroom this side of the Arctic Circle. The landlord hadn't carried out any of the agreed renovations and it now looked even worse than when I had first seen it. My fellow housemates were not impressed as I showed them around their new home and I just about prevented a mutiny by promising to ring the landlord and demand that she at least give the place a good clean. Amy looked at me like a disappointed schoolkid who had begged their parents for a pair of Nike trainers in order to be 'part of the gang' but had instead been presented with a pair of Nicks with the justification that they were 'just the same as Nike's but a lot cheaper.' Amy blamed me for us living in that dump of a house. I know she did because she told me on numerous occasions. I liked the house because it was cheap. My room was even cheaper than the rest as I had agreed to take the dreaded downstairs bedroom. Although this did mean that I would often be kept awake by my fellow students walking along our street, attempting to recreate an episode of Supermarket Sweep, with an abandoned shopping trolley, at 3am.

We were still love's young dream as we entered the house but I had insisted that we had separate rooms. We needed to study and I wanted my own desk to hide under and listen to Morrissey. I thought the space would do us good. It's not as if we'd spent much time that summer in the same bedroom as I was in the spare room whenever I visited hers. Her dad had changed tactics and stayed up late into the night patrolling the hallway, making sure that I didn't get the opportunity to corrupt his darling daughter. When Amy came to stop at ours I was meant to sleep on the floor of my room while she had the bed. As my room was right next door to Mum and Dads, that was usually how it stayed as well. Any passion that we wanted to fit in either had to be quickly concluded while my parents nipped to Tesco's, or was al fresco in the fields that surrounded her village. Now we had two rooms in which to either be together or on our own. It seemed like the only logical arrangement. Despite an initial sulk, Amy eventually agreed.

On only our 2nd night in Wyverne Road, things between Amy and I took their first backward step since we'd rid Matt from our lives. The 4 of us had gone to the pub as an impromptu 'housewarming but out of the house' that I'd organised to take everyone's mind off the state of our new home. At closing time, full of the joys of student life and Fosters, we came back from the pub to find a large patch of rainwater on my bedroom floor and the unmistakable cloying stench of damp in the living room. This was not a good sign, and neither was the withering look that Amy cast in my direction. She shook her head, tapped her lips to mine as opposed to kissing me and stomped off up the stairs.

In the middle of the night, Amy ventured downstairs to use the only toilet in the house. On the return journey, whilst crossing the kitchen floor, she stepped on something soft, but rather than turn on the light and risk waking me, she went back upstairs to her room. When she turned on her bedroom light she saw the squished remains of 3 slugs slowly dripping from her bare foot. She promptly threw up all over the floor.

I was awoken by what sounded like an urban riot going on above my head and bounded up the stairs into Amy's room to be confronted by a wailing banshee trashing the place. If Linda Blair's character in The Exorcist had hailed from Cambridge, she would have looked exactly like Amy did that night.

As she threw things around the room, she hissed at me; 'This house is a shithole and it's your fault that I live here and have slugs on my bloody feet. You fucking tight wanker, making us live here, just so you can save a few measly quid to spend on fucking CD's by shit indie bands. You're meant to love me 'so much', what a load of bollocks that is. If you loved me, you wouldn't make me live here would you, WOULD YOU?'

I didn't say a word, which appeared to make things worse.

'Well? Say SOMETHING!'

I didn't say a word, mainly because my brain was stuck on the thought that my copy of "Vauxhall & I" was on the shelf that was next in line for her to trash. If that CD got harmed there really would be trouble.

Watching the woman you love weeping uncontrollably, with a combination of sick and squashed slug at her feet, her worldly goods scattered all around her, should provoke a mature response. I should have told her it would all be ok, cleaned her up, put her to bed and held her until she fell asleep. Instead, I was annoyed that she'd shouted at me and stormed out of the room. I ran downstairs, pulled on my jeans, my Billy Bragg "Don't Try This At Home" sweatshirt, grabbed my Discman and left the house, slamming the door as I went. I got 5 yards before hearing her window fly open, and turned to see her leaning as far out of the crumbling wooden frame as she dare whilst cackling and applauding me. I didn't turn back again. I pounded the early morning streets wondering if this was the beginning of the end or simply the end of the beginning. Couples couldn't stay in that blissful state of the early days forever, I knew that, but I hadn't been expecting my mild mannered girlfriend to turn psycho on our 2nd night in a new home. By 4am, I was pretty sure she would be asleep so made my way back to the house, locked my door and crawled under the duvet.

I woke at lunchtime, relieved that she hadn't crept into my room in the early hours and put squashed slugs up my nose. I knew she would be at a lecture so, for a minute or two, wondered if last night might all be forgotten and we could get back to normal. That lingering thought was shattered when I opened my bedroom door, and in tumbled my smashed and torn copy of "Vauxhall & I". She had leant it against the door so it would be the first thing I saw when I opened it. I was fuming and determined to get my revenge for such a callous act of cultural vandalism. I'd have rather that she'd come in and put the squashed slugs up my nose.

Later that day, after visiting the library and the café to read the paper, I wandered into the poster fair that was being held in our SU building. Our SU seemed to be holding these fairs every week, and the poster was taking over from the band t-shirt as the way that students showed their allegiances. When I saw the huge Beth Orton poster, of her dressed in a Jackson Pollock inspired dress, I knew I had to have it. I'd had a crush on her since the release of the magnificent 'Trailer Park' earlier that year. Amy would take the piss out of Ms Orton's Norfolk accent and question what I found attractive about her. With this in mind, I knew that buying the poster and placing it on the wall right next to my bed would annoy her. My revenge would be petty but it would be complete.

When Amy returned from her archaeology lecture that evening, I greeted her with my usual cheery: "Alright Indiana?" but she didn't respond. She went to walk straight up the stairs but upon glancing into my room, saw my new poster and burst out laughing. She pushed open the door and said:

'Is this your weird idea of revenge for me smashing your CD?

Putting up a poster of a woman you fancy next to your bed? You really are a loser. What are you going to do, lay there with me on top of you and gaze at her? You're so pathetic it's funny.

Anyway, do you want to come up town? You and this crappy house have depressed me so much that I need to buy something to cheer myself up. You can wander round the record shops for a couple of hours whilst I buy a new dress from Top Shop then we can go to the pub, get drunk and try and forget about slugs and Beth soddin' Orton.'

How could I possibly have refused such an offer? That was it, our first major row over and done with. Over an Aftershock toast in Metros later that night, we vowed to, 'never have another argument ever again'.

Over the next few weeks we kept to our no argument pledge and normal, loving service was resumed. As with any couple, we still had a whole heap of issues though. Our problem list included our slum house, homesickness and the fact that by November we were having to cope with one of the worst winters since the last ice age.

As a boy from the Fens, a patch of East Anglia where the land is so flat that a molehill really does resemble a mountain, Cardiff was a shock to the system. I didn't ever acclimatise to the bone snapping cold of a Welsh winter or opening our front door and seeing a snow-topped hill seemingly only a couple of miles away. In Talybont this hadn't been a problem, as the communal heating was constantly set to match the temperature of a hospital ward. Even in the depths of February, with snow and ice on the ground, we would be sat in our kitchen in shorts and t-shirts, moaning about the cloying heat. In our house in Wyverne Road it was very different. If we managed to persuade the heating to work, usually by whacking the boiler with a lump hammer, the 4 of us would huddle around the only two radiators that actually gave out any heat whilst passing round a medicinal bottle of cherry brandy.

The damp was creeping up the walls of every downstairs room. Any clothes left exposed to the air would quickly develop an unknown species of white moss. We complained to the landlord, Reenie, about the situation, with me ringing her daily to give her disaster updates but she was much smarter than us. Reenie was a wily old fox who would play the, "I'm just an old lady, I don't know anything about anything" card when it suited her, to distract us from threats of witholding our rent. Alternatively, if we complained about the heating, she would come to the house, make a point of taking off her hat, coat, scarf and gloves, sit down and proclaim; "Nonsense, it is lovely and warm in here", as her teeth chattered and her lips began to match the colour of her hair.

The house was dragging Amy into a stagnant pool of depression and I didn't have a clue how to wade in and drag her out. As always, I turned to Morrissey for answers. The Smiths song "Jeane" became our anthem, well my anthem, for Wyverne Road, with its talk of ice on sinks and bare cupboards. I would play it all the time, singing it to Amy and, if she was happy she would laugh. If the house was getting her down she would weep and throw things at me. She would lay on my bed, wrapped up against the elements in my two, always slightly damp, duvets as I danced around the room serenading her. I was doing my best. It was a crap, immature best but it was all I had.

I wasn't letting the house get me down. As Amy quite rightly pointed out, it's cheap rent meant that I had money to spend on CD's, and I was now even cutting back on food and beer to buy more music every week.

I also loved the fact that living in such a decrepit old house allowed me to live life as if I was in the dark comedic world of a Smiths song. I didn't see anything worrying or pathetic in telling my girlfriend that, even as she cried herself to sleep.

Then in December of '96, SFA released a song of true genius, in the form of the behemoth, f-word filled, "The Man Don't Give a Fuck" and everything seemed right in our world again. Not many songs could have that kind of momunental impact on life, but this was no ordinary tune. It was a glorious song, the kind that picked you up, spun you around until you felt a bit sick before smashing your serotonin levels with a hammer and taking over control of your limbs to achieve its own gloriously perverted aims. Amy and I would put it on in my room and dance around while the windows rattled with the bass. As with so many truly gargantuan songs it was even better when played live. We went to the triumphant end of year Manics gig at the Cardiff International Arena with SFA and Catatonia supporting. SFA blew us all away that night with 40 minutes of scuzzed up rock 'n' roll perfection, culminating in a glorious 10 minute version of that song.

By the time we got back to The Beat Bar for their late night indie disco, we were buzzing our bits off. Amy and I decided to mark the occasion by deciding to visit the 'bloke in the corner of the bar' and enjoy a Mitsubishi enhanced evening. We followed the classic sequence of events and were frustrated when, half an hour after having taken a half each, we agreed that 'nothing's happening, these must be duds'. Frustrated, we decided to neck the other halves. Ten minutes later we were shaking our heads at each other, silently fuming that we had paid £12 each for aspirin. Then the opening beats to 'The Man Don't Give A Fuck' filled the room and my internal headlights switched in an instant from sidelights to full beam. For the 4 minutes and 48 seconds duration of the song, we jumped up and down, gurning and attempting to kiss while pogoing. With the venue lights projecting violent arcs of purple and red, I assumed I was just tripping when I thought I saw blood all down my front and so carried on dancing. It was only at the end of the song, as my now super modelesque girlfriend gave me a euphoric snog that we realised we had a problem. I looked at Amy's mouth and with wide eyed wonder, rather than alarm, told her;

'Wow, you look like a vampire, you've got blood all over your lips, that looks cool, really cool.'

As she attempted to get the auto focus function for her eyes working again, she looked deep into my open mouth;

'I think it's you Jay, you've got a mouth full of blood and it's all over your top,' she said as she bounced up and down next to me, as 'Girls & Boys' smashed into our ears.

I looked down at my newly purchased grey SFA t-shirt and saw that the front had turned a beautiful crimson colour. I put my hand to my lips and felt warm, comforting, velvet like blood flowing out of a gash that felt intriguingly deep as I pushed my finger in. My brain was telling me that it was a blood fountain, a special gift from the lead Furry Animal and that it was to be loved and cherished.

'Jay, JAY - are you ok? You've been stood holding your lip and not saying anything for ages.'

I stood and tried to rationalise my options. I had to make the night carry on, the bar was still open and we were flying, we couldn't waste it. The solution seemed spectacularly simple. Amy went to the bar and I went to get a plaster from the friendly bouncers. We spent the next 2 hours buzzing, going crazy to any tune the DJ served up, while I kept pushing the Elastoplast full of blood back onto my gaping wound.

The next minute it was 5am and the two of us were in our shower, fully dressed, singing Stone Roses tunes. As the water smashed into my tender lip, I sat and watched the blood slowly wash down the plug hole for what may well have been an hour but was more likely to have been a minute or two. With more love within our frames than we knew what to do with, we looked at each other under this red hot shower, me with blood flowing from my lips, her looking like a giant panda thanks to the combination of water and mascara, we burst out laughing and had a big, soggy hug.

As Amy got undressed, I examined my battle scarred face. It was painfully obvious from the shape of the wound in my lip that I had bitten down on it, with a lot of force, during the euphoria of 'The Man Don't Give A Fuck' and my tooth had gone deep into the flesh.

I put some butterfly strips across it that I'd found in Amys medical box and collapsed onto her bed in a fit of giggles. Realising we were both still under the influence of the night before, we used the last of our chemical energy to please each other, in that intense, fuzzy yet almost unhuman way that only E can produce, before falling asleep wrapped in each other for the next 7 hours.

After a couple of weeks and 3 packets of sterile strips my lip finally healed, though the indentation of my tooth remained as a scar and a permanent reminder of a blinding night.

1997

Your Ex-Boyfriend Is At The Door

OUR Christmas break from University wasn't quite the romantic snow and sex filled holiday that the previous year had been but we still met up, drank mulled wine and discussed ways to make Amy happier. I didn't have any strong suggestions on how to achieve this, other than to borrow Neil's standard advice, 'I'll get us another pint in.' I knew the house was getting her down and I suspected that I was as well but there was nothing I could do about either of those, so decided to keep quiet.

Upon our return to Cardiff we found that the days appeared to be getting ever shorter and the temperature was dropping like a Morrissey single's chart position in its second week of release. One morning, Amy still hadn't surfaced by 10am, so I went up to her room and, as always, went in without knocking. I found her in bed, shivering despite 2 duvets, multiple layers of clothes and an electric fan heater dangerously less than 6 inches from her face. She was weeping dejected tears of ice and I realised that I had to do something. Lacking in real inspiration, I gave her a warming cuddle, made her a coffee and ran her a bath, having scrubbed the worst of the grime off it first. She kissed me on the cheek with her pale blue lips and seemed to cheer up after her dip. I knew it wasn't going to last of course, she was desperately unhappy with our home and a bath, even with bubbles in, couldn't solve that permanently. I was still blissfully happy despite the cold. I had my cheap room, towering piles of CD's to sort into alphabetical order and my ever loving girlfriend.

I was snapped out of this little daydream and back into the reality of the situation in late January when I came home from an exam, with the intention of taking Amy out for a pint in the warm pub, but instead got no reply when I shouted "Are you here, Indiana?" I went into my room and saw, with a sense of foreboding, a note that I instantly recognised as being from Amy thanks to her spidery, Morrisseyesque handwriting. It read:

Jay

I can't take this place anymore. I've finished my exams and can't spend another night here. I know you are happy living like this but I'm not. I love you but I can't live with you like this.

I'm going home to my folks and I'm not sure if or when I will be coming back.

Feel free to ring me if you want to....

Love Always

Indiana

X

PS – I bet after the initial shock of this note fades, you will be thinking about which Moz tracks you can listen to whilst clutching a bottle of lager and thinking how tough the world is on you.

I sat there dumbfounded. I hadn't for one minute considered that she would leave me here and go home. How could she leave me? Was that how little she thought of our relationship? How could she just up and leave without saying goodbye or giving me the chance to persuade her to stay? I read the note again and again trying to find some hidden meaning but the only solace I could find was that she had signed it "Indiana", rather than Amy. Slim pickings indeed. She was right though, I put Moz on the stereo, drew the curtains and revelled in the dark to the likes of "Jack The Ripper" and "Southpaw".

Later that evening, I went up to her room to discover that she had packed a few clothes, some of her books and, obviously, made a quick exit. I decided that I would stay in her room until she returned, partly through some strange romantic notion but mainly because it was much nicer than mine, even with the distinct smell of sick and slugs buried deep in the carpet.

Sitting on her bed that night, morosely drinking hot chocolate and feeling sorry for myself, I noticed out of the corner of my eye that she had left behind her copy of Suede's "Coming Up". Now I was worried, as she loved that album. It had become our album, listening to Brett Anderson's tales of glittering, battered urban landscapes had become an integral part of our lives in this shitty old house. We would listen to songs from it every day, sometimes dancing round the room, sometimes laying on the bed in contented silence, sometimes crying. That album had everything and she had left it behind. She had left me behind. Like Amy had done so many nights before in that bed, I wrapped the duvets around me and cried myself to a bitter, dreamless sleep.

The next evening, I found myself back in her room with a morbid determination to feel like the victim of the situation. I put on "Coming Up", laid back on the bed that smelt of her and let the songs sweep over me. From the brash, us against the world love affair of "Trash", to the anthem we used to sing about the cool kids at the university, "The Beautiful Ones". Then came the haunting beauty of "By The Sea" hit me hard in the chest and in a pit of self loathing I mentally beat myself up for pushing her away.

I reminisced about when, a few months earlier, we had gone to see Suede on the 'Coming Up' tour at Newport Leisure Centre.

Amy had loved it, went crazier than I had ever seen her before, with her bobbed hair matted to her sweaty forehead, totally lost in the emotion of the gig. She had looked so beautiful, in a manic Suede induced fever and I don't think I ever loved her as much as when, whilst waiting for the encore to begin, her lips planted themselves against mine and she said, 'Get me a pint sweetheart, I'm sweating my tits off here.'

Those good times now seemed like they belonged in the first movie of our relationship trilogy and that we were now in the depths of the convoluted, badly scripted 2nd film in the series.

I didn't write or call straight away. I wallowed for a full 4 days. On the 5th day a postcard arrived with a photo of the Eiffel Tower on the front. I knew without turning it over it was from Amy, as she was desperate for us to visit Paris. On the back she had simply written:

Not missing me then?

Was it meant to be dark humour or was she warning me that I had better call or write soon? Either way, it made me smile and realise that she was still thinking about me. I gathered up all the money I had in my emergency fund and all the silver coins from her 'change pot' walked to Cardiff Central to buy a ticket and boarded a train headed for Cambridge. Five hours, two trains and a bus journey later, I arrived at her parents front door, rang the bell and hoped that her dad didn't answer the door.

Her dad answered the door and, without acknowledging my existence, turned and shouted up the stairs:

'Amy, your ex-boyfriend is at the door!'

I couldn't help but burst out laughing. He looked at me with absolute disdain. I could see his eyes asking how his beautiful daughter was going out with the buffoon stood before him. That just made me want to laugh some more.

Amy bounded down the stairs, made a point of kissing me whilst her dad tutted and walked back into the living room, then said; "You took your time didn't you, I've been sat here all packed for 3 days waiting for you to come and get me". After a quick chat on the doorstep about; "things that need to change in our relationship" (Amy) and humble apologies (Me), we were out of the front door and on our way back to South Wales.

Even to an idiot like me it was obvious that I needed to get back into Amy's good books and quickly. I decided that a trip to the city of love would be in order. On a frozen February morning, with our heating not working again, I took her out to breakfast at our local greasy spoon café and proudly announced:

'Look, I know I can be a knobhead sometimes and I know the house is my fault and it's been getting you down so, to make up for it, I'm taking you to Paris.'

When she leant over the table to hug and kiss me, I was happy. I even ignored the fact that her green Benetton scarf had dipped into my fried egg. When she began to quietly cry with tears of joy and thanks, I began to feel a little guilty. I knew that Amy was dreaming of a weekend of aeroplanes, 4* hotels, fine dining and romance. Instead, I had booked us on a £35 a head, 30 hour coach trip to Paris. We would be leaving Cardiff at 3am to drive to Dover before boarding the ferry to Calais. Upon reaching French soil, the coach would drive to Paris and drop us off in the Place De La Concorde. We would then have a full 12 hours to explore the city before the coach picked us up and began the long journey back to Wales. I didn't fill her in with all the details at the café, mainly because she was elated at the thought of going to Paris and wanted to head into town to buy a guide book.

After buying the book, we then spent the rest of the day sat in the SU bar planning our adventure. She was happier than I had seen her for months and I couldn't bring myself to give her the full details of our trip. I woke at 3am, looked over at her having the first decent night's sleep she'd had in Cardiff for months and thought that only I could make such a mess of taking my girlfriend to Paris.

It was when she woke me next morning with a cheery "Bonjour" and a plate of fresh croissants that I knew I had to come clean about the reality of our trip. I persuaded her to get back under the duvet, wrapped my arms around her and, with an entirely inappropriate grin on my face, told her about the coach journey. As her face began to drop, I adjusted the grin downwards ever so slightly and quietly promised that we would do everything she wanted to; visit the Louvre, the Arc De Triomphe, Eiffel Tower and drink coffee on the Champs-Eleysee. We would just have to do them all quickly. She offered me a tight, watery smile and through slightly gritted teeth said "It will be wonderful". As I drifted back to sleep, I could feel her laid in my arms gently beginning to cry. I had no words, no way of improving the situation, so I kept my eyes closed and hoped that sleep would take me quickly.

As she was quite perky when I woke up an hour later, I thought that I had got away with it. That was until I overheard her talking to Lou in our kitchen a few days later:

Lou: 'That's brilliant he's taking you to Paris. He knows how much you want to go there and how unhappy you are in this house, he's trying at least."

Amy – laughing: "Oh yeah, a 30 hour coach trip, with him moaning about the cost of everything at service stations, on the ferry and in Paris, I can't wait! Why does he have to make everything a bloody war of attrition? We both know he will spoil this trip before we even get off the coach.'

She knew me far too well. She did, however, still look a little surprised to find me in our rancid, slug infested kitchen the evening before we left, making sandwiches. She looked over at my festival rucksack which was filled with cans of Apple Tango and Mini Cheddars before gruffly enquiring:

'So, just so I'm clear on this - we're going all the way to Paris, the culinary capital of the world, to drink Apple Tango and eat cheddar cheese sandwiches?"'

Me: 'No, don't be silly. I made the sarnies with Red Leicester as I know it's your favourite.'

I diligently went back to making the sandwiches and only just heard her singing the Pet Shop Boys tune, "What Have I Done To Deserve This?" as she walked away.

On a numbingly cold Cardiff early morning, we boarded the coach and headed to Dover. With a choppy ferry crossing and a further 3 hour coach journey negotiated, we arrived in Paris at midday with strict instructions to meet the coach at midnight back at the Place De La Concorde.

Eager to get started, we speed walked to the Champs-Élysées and gazed in wonder at the wide street and the Arc De Triomphe proudly standing at the top of the hill. I would happily have stayed at the majestic Arc all day but, as with Nelsons Column, the fact that it was surrounded by heaving, smoking traffic spoilt the serenity of the scene a little.The adrenaline rush of being in Paris and fulfilling a dream, meant that Amy shook off her tiredness and apprehension and was wandering around with a permanent smile. I knew I had to ride this particular wave for all it was worth. She was giddy with childlike excitement as we wandered down the Champs-Élysées. With our lust for life at an all-time high, we decided to go crazy and have coffee and frites in a café. It was a stunning location and, like all cafes that are in such places, their prices were even more stunning than the view. I had pledged to treat Amy to this mini feast so, even when presented with the horror of the bill, I calmly paid with shaking hands and a bundle of francs.

After that open wallet surgery, my mental arithmetic told me that, aside from the 8 francs needed to gain entry to the

Louvre, all my cash had gone. From here on in, unless Amy was paying, we were on the emergency rucksack rations.

As we walked into The Louvre, Amy was ecstatic and, for the first time in months, I felt like a good boyfriend and a decent human being. We spent 5 hours in the museum and I found the first couple of those fascinating. By the end of the 4th hour, as Amy was still finding wonder in every painting or statue, I just wanted a beer and a sit down. After going a little crazy in the souvenir shop and indulging her love of Monet postcards, she finally took pity on me and said; 'C'mon, let's find a bar. I'll treat you to a beer for bringing me to this amazing place and not moaning all day.'

We made our way to a tiny hostelry overlooking the Seine and, as Amy looked through her book on Monet, I sat and enjoyed every mouthful of my ice cold beer. I took some mental photos of the scene, silently storing them as credit against future arguments. I was having a drink with my girlfriend in the middle of Paris, only an idiot wouldn't enjoy that and, despite my multiple personality defects, I wasn't an idiot.

Amy left me sat at the table, gazing at the river and daydreaming, and went to pay the bill. It was when she came back and proudly announced, "Well that's the last of my money spent", it dawned on me that the remaining 6 hours we had in Paris were not going to be as much fun as the first 6. Here we were, in one of the most expensive cities in the world, with less than a franc between us.

Rather than act like the mature, urbane 20 year old man that had been on display so far that day, I went into grumpy toddler mode. We left the bar and moved to a bench in the vast municipal park next to The Louvre. I didn't say a word for an hour. Instead I twisted my darkest thoughts into a knot and forensically examined the contrast between sitting in a park now and when we used to do so during our first year together. Then it had been excited chatter, with arms and legs wrapped around each other. Now here we were in Paris, the city of love, sitting in silence.

With the biting cold of the evening descending, I decided that we may as well go and wait for the coach at the Place De La Concorde. So, we sat, not saying a word, watching the traffic hurtle around us. I turned my ever darkening thoughts inward and pondered how I had managed to turn a trip to Paris into such a disaster. The contrast between the heartbroken look on Amys face, as we sat there waiting, compared to when I first told her about our trip was not lost on me.

I'll Just Consult Moz

BACK in Cardiff, it was now clear to everyone, including us, that our relationship was becoming a shitty, spiteful mess. We had created a monster which initially had been full of love, lust and life but had now found its black hearted alter ego and we had long since lost control of it. We would go from being riotously in love to desperately unhappy in the midst of a single argument. I would retreat to my room and my stereo, Amy would pack her rucksack and run back to Cambridge. Neither of us had any clue how to heal our relationship's wounds so, rather than talk to each other, she sought advice from her mum and I consulted Moz. Then on one glorious spring evening, for one night only, everything seemed to change.

Everyone in our house had fallen under the spell cast by Tony Blair. It wasn't so much that we believed in him, more that he could offer us something different, something that wasn't the Conservatives. We knew that, as D:Ream sang, "Things Can Only Get Better". As the election results came in during the night of 1st/2nd May, we danced around our front room, ecstatic that, for the first time since we were toddlers, we wouldn't be ruled by a Tory government. As Michael Portillo got the news of his seat being lost live on the TV, we glugged from our specially purchased bottle of Asti Spumante. I don't think I'd have been any happier if England had won the World Cup. I felt full of hope for the future of my beloved country and our relationship. The joy of an election win inspired Amy and I to clamber into the same bed for the first time in weeks and all seemed well with the world.

The next morning she got up and asked me to look away whilst she got dressed, before kissing me on the cheek and heading to her lecture. It appeared we weren't in the midst of a new beginning after all.

With Amy away from Cardiff for long periods and my degree seemingly not needing any assignments from me in the 2nd year, I needed something to fill my days. It was the age of the music fanzine so I decided to write my own. I dragged in Neil, Lou and Amy (when she deigned us with her presence) and "The Blue" indie music fanzine was born. It sold for a very reasonable 45p plus 25p postage and packing. It was a lot of hard work just to sell 67 copies, hence why it only ran for two editions. I also ended up managing a band from the West Midlands called 'Solo 70' for a few months. Well, I say managed, I didn't really do much other than interview them for the fanzine and get them a couple of interviews with other 'zines but it made me feel important. I had stumbled across them when they played a gig in Cardiff at our local pub and noticed that Jon Baker was their guitarist. Jon had been the original guitarist in The Charlatans, played on their debut album and had a writing credit on "Sproston Green". In my eyes, that made him indie royalty. I talked to him after the gig with wild eyed enthusiasm, he mentioned they needed a manager and that was it, job secured. I left my illustrious position a couple of months later when the band decided that, in order to generate much needed publicity, they were going to change their name to 'Universal', in the hope that the record company of the same name would sue them. I couldn't be a part of such behaviour, I was all about the music, so I resigned. I had been such an ineffective manager I doubt they even noticed.

For Amy and I, our best times together during this period, were at gigs. She would regularly tell me that us going to gigs was the only time she could be sure that I would be in a good mood. I even peeled off the clingfilm that encased my wallet and paid for Amy to get into plenty of them, in an attempt to make her happy. The best of those gigs was when Beck played at our SU in March. Riding high on the back of the success of the triumphant 'Odelay', he came in and forced everyone in the crowd to dance, gyrate and fall under his spell. As we jumped around to the likes of 'Where It's At' and 'Devils Haircut', we were a couple smack bang in love again. The music and alcohol combination stripped the bitter times away and we transported back to being the couple locked in her room, desperate to hold each other. I even missed the joyous crowd-led rendition of "Loser" to get her a pint from the bar. If that wasn't a demonstration of true love then I didn't know what was.

1997 isn't remembered as a classic year for indie music, but for us it was an illustrious period with some sublime albums being released that year:

Spiritualized – *Ladies & Gentlemen We Are Floating in Space*

Teenage Fanclub – *Songs From Northern Britain*

Nick Cave & The Bad Seeds – *The Boatman's Call*

Radiohead – *OK Computer*

Super Furry Animals – *Radiator*

The Charlatans – *Tellin' Stories*

Primal Scream – *Vanishing Point*

Morrissey – *Maladjusted*

Spritualized's - "Ladies & Gentlemen…." was a fascinating album, full of huge songs in a pill box style cover, with the CD held in a blister pack as if it was an extra large paracetamol. I'd liked the odd track on each of their previous releases but on "Ladies & Gentlemen….", Jason Pierce had created a scene of love, loss and getting trashed. The music press couldn't help but reiterate at every opportunity that the album was Pierce's broken hearted love letter to his ex-partner and keyboard player in the band, Kate Radley, who had left him and then married Richard Ashcroft from The Verve. Pierce denied that was the meaning but, to be honest, it just made the maudlin, increasingly lovelorn loser in me adore "Ladies & Gentlemen..." even more.

I got into the habit of getting a few bottles of beer, lighting twenty or so tea lights, lying on the floor of my room and listening to "Ladies & Gentlemen..." on repeat. Sometimes Amy came in and, without saying a word, would lay on my bed, take a bottle of beer and we'd listen to the album in contented silence. Once or twice she even came in, silently undressed and we would act like normal students. In the background, this soundtrack of drugs and heartbreak would prickle against our naked skin, seeping into every desperate attempt we made to satisfy each other. At other times, if she was annoyed with me or trying to study, she would bang on the floor of her bedroom and urge me to "turn that bloody Spiritualized album down". For about 6 months, "Ladies & Gentlemen.." was one of those extra special albums that seemed to fit my every mood.

Morrissey's "Maladjusted" got a battering by the music critics upon its release but I loved it. Songs like "Wide To Receive" and "Satan Rejected My Soul" were classic Moz and I spent many hours in my room, learning the words and throwing myself around as Amy tried to revise next to me.

Teenage Fanclub's "Songs From Northern Britain" was my album of the year. It was this glorious band at their melodic, harmony driven pop best. The first bars of songs like "Aint That Enough", would bring a grin to my face and make me feel happy to be alive. Amy didn't really fall under their spell but that didn't stop me playing that album to her on a daily basis. I would tell her that it contained a song that fitted any situation that our relationship stumbled into. When she moaned at me for only wanting to drink in 'old man's pubs', or for refusing to go to

'The Astoria' nightclub, I would play her "I Don't Want Control of You". When we argued in her room, shouting increasingly hurtful things to each other and ending up collapsing into her bed in a red-eyed ball of fear and regret, I would play "Your Love Is The Place Where I Come From", in a ham-fisted attempt to show her how much I still cared. I truly believed that continually playing those songs would help solve the ever multiplying problems that our relationship had acquired.

TFC had always been an immaculate live band. From the first time I'd seen them at Glastonbury in 1993, I'd always made a point of going to their gigs whenever possible. My favourite Teenage Fanclub pilgramage took place in October 1997 at the Anson Room in Bristol. As we were both big fans, Lou and I decided to make the short train journey from Cardiff to take in the gig.

Lou was an English Literature student with a prodigious appetite for alcohol. Lager, cider or meths, she would guzzle it down then tell you how magnificent London, Spurs and The Manics were. On the afternoon of the gig she had been in the pub for a few hours, debating with her course mates the merits of some 200 year old book or other, so was half-cut by the time we boarded the train.

Upon arrival in Bristol, even after a quick nap on the train, it was obvious that Lou was struggling to stand up straight but she insisted on ploughing on to the pub for a 'livener' then onto the Anson Rooms. Undeterred by her limbs not working in conjunction with her brain, she carried on drinking until Teenage Fanclub hit the stage. They were on stunning form with tight harmonies and perfect song choices. It was one of the best gigs that I'd ever been to. I was bouncing around the place, loving every second of their set but kept catching a glimpse of Lou, who was stood shaking her head and muttering to herself.

At the end of the triumphant gig, with the elated crowd howling for more, all Lou would say to me was; "That was amazing and shit, amazing and shit, amazing and shit". I decided to take inspiration from Neil when faced with a friend appearing to have a crisis and went to the bar to get her another pint whilst waiting for her sanity to return. As we sat and supped in silence, the band wandered out from the backstage area to get a well earned drink. They had been so fantastic that I couldn't resist going over to congratulate them and get my new "Songs From Northern Britain" t-shirt signed. As I chatted my fan-boy gibberish to the band, Lou got up from her chair, holding the sides for support and shouted across the bar:

'Don't talk to them wankers Jay, they mimed their way through that gig. No band can sing like that, I know they mimed. Everyone else fell for it but not me.'

Cue nervous laughter from the band and me.

'Don't laugh, I know you were miming and I want my money back.'

With a quick, mumbled apology to everyone present, I bundled a still shouting Lou out into the sobering October air and into a taxi. The next day, she had just about rehydrated her senses by teatime and over a hair of the dog pint she insisted to Amy and Neil that; 'No band could be that good, they had to be miming.'

Teenage Fanclub really were that good.

Amy and I knew by the spring of 1997 that our relationship was in the kind of trouble that alcohol and sex could now only prolong rather than save. We were still in love but our arguments were getting feistier and the silences lasting ever longer. Deep down, we knew that the blissful future that we'd planned in the early days of our relationship was now never going to become a reality. So, we just didn't talk about our future anymore, not even vague discussions about what either of us would do when university finished for us in 12 months' time. We just pretended that the future didn't exist. As usual I looked to music to help.

I would play her Teenage Fanclub's "Start Again" and she would chuckle and whisper loving asides like: "If I start again Jay, it won't be with you" and "Why can't I split up with you? I really want to but I can't seem to do it. I wish sometimes that I didn't love you, it would be easy then."

To take our minds off our relationship we both threw ourselves into our work. With no love or social life to distract me, I became engrossed in my course, mainly thanks to the inspirational teaching of my Course Director, Paul Lodge. I would sit engrossed in his lectures and then head off alone for long, warm afternoons in the Humanities library reading about Scargill, the NHS and Nye Bevan. I was still going to gigs but Amy had decided, in an ironic twist, that I was now better off going to them on my own. I even bought her a ticket for Paul Weller's outdoor gig in Cardiff Bay but she flatly refused to come along as she had studying to do. I went on my own, got plastered, thought Weller and Gene were both superb and didn't speak a word to anyone (other than the bar staff) all day.

That summer was going to be a busy one as I had somehow persuaded Amy to come to accompany me to two festivals. For my 4th Glastonbury and Amy's 1st, we went as a foursome with Jacko and his girlfriend, Claire. My previous Glastonbury's had been played out on a festival site bathed in sunshine and smiles but that year was to prove very different. The heavens opened on the Thursday evening as we pitched our tents and it didn't stop raining for a minute of the next 48 hours. The site was transformed from an idyllic, baked earth scene to a quagmire in a matter of hours. I'd thought that I'd got wet and cold at Reading in 1992 but that was a week on the beach in Ibiza compared to this. On the Friday morning we saw people still so smashed from the night before that they hadn't even noticed that the tent they had gone to sleep in had blown away in the night. By Saturday morning the festival authorities were using canoes to rescue people from the worst affected areas of the site. A lad in the tent next to ours was diagnosed with trench foot by the medical staff and loaded into a muddy ambulance for treatment.

The only thing we could do was get drunk and make the best of it. We pulled on our DM boots, took a swig from the bottle of port I had brought with me and headed out into the mud. It was bloody hard work getting about the site, wanting to see bands but being unable to slog through the mud in time to see their set was a frequent and annoying occurrence. The four of us used all our reserves of English spirit and pluck to determinedly enjoy ourselves. As always for me, Glasto was first and foremost about the music. One of the highlights was an afternoon Ray Davies set where he set out to cheer up the shivering masses with some Kinks singalongs. As the crowd cheered and attempted to prise their feet from the glue pot, Amy and I crooned our way through the glorious "Waterloo Sunset".

Late on Saturday night, we took our place in the primordial goo that had previously been the Pyramid Stage field to watch the headliners, the much heralded Radiohead. A weary crowd, battered by the weather, was picked up by Oxford's finest as they threw themselves headlong into a intoxicating set. It was a performance that took your mind away from the cold and wet and proved to be a real 'I was there' Glasto moment. For 90 minutes every member of the crowd was captivated, from the mass shoutalong to "Creep", through to the lighters in the for "Fake Plastic Trees" (70,000 people deciding not to notice or care that "Fake Plastic Trees" was one of the least romantic songs ever written.) It was that kind of night. It was impossible to dance due to the mud but you could turn around and see thousands of people vigorously swaying and waving their arms around. As they left the stage for the final time and we stood clapping our hands red raw, I thought back to their gig in Peterborough supporting the Frank & Walters and felt a strange twinge of pride at how far they had come in 4 years.

None of us could sleep after watching that performance. We knew that we had witnessed something special and wanted to keep the buzz going. We went back to our tents and experienced the unbridled joy of taking off our boots and sipping on a warm lager. The downpour finally stopped at 3am so, with a sheet of dry tarpaulin to lay on the floor, Amy and I headed down to the front of the Pyramid Stage. I had wittered on for hours about how much I loved sitting there and I was ecstatic to finally share it with her. The festival bosses had laid down tons of straw in an attempt to soak up the mud so, with the tarpaulin laid down, we were even able to sit down right up against the stage barrier on the dry but squidgy ground. I felt happier than I had done in a long time. Sat in my special place, I looked at Amy properly for the first time in months. I didn't think about the future, or our arguments or how much she annoyed me when she didn't put the Flora back in the fridge, I just looked at her. I sensed the merest hint of the same feeling I had felt the first time I met her in the queue for The Tavern almost 2 years previous. She was still my girl, I hadn't totally ballsed it up. Huddled together as the sun was rising and with the lager all gone, we fell into a contended sleep in each other's arms.

I awoke a couple of hours later to find that we had been encircled by the lake of mud and were now cut off from civilisation. Thankfully, a kind steward spotted our predicament and instructed a passing tractor to dump some bales of hay so that he could build a makeshift bridge for us to escape over.

That Glastonbury was the first festival where I saw people diving headfirst into the mud and sludge. They would normally do such a bloody stupid thing to get themselves noticed by a passing TV camera or press photographer. My only thought was, "No matter how drunk, stoned or desperate to be on TV you are, in about 10 minutes time you are going to be bloody freezing and picking 3 day old noodles out of your hair". By the Sunday afternoon, we'd had enough of slopping around in the mud. This, coupled with the fact that Sting was headlining the

Pyramid Stage that night, persuaded us to leave early. After watching the customary Billy Bragg Glasto performance, we decided to pack up our tents and begin the long journey home.

The train from Castle Cary to Birmingham New Street was full of festival-goers who, like us, didn't want to watch Sting attempt a mass tantric sex session and were encrusted in mud. On the journey from Birmingham to Peterborough however, on a now warm, dry summer evening, we looked like swamp creatures let loose on a train. When we eventually got home, Mum initially wanted me to stand in the garden while Dad hosed me down. Even he realised that this was taking her OCD-like desire for a clean house too far and I was allowed to get undressed at the back door and run to the shower. Amy was allowed to simply take off her shoes and walk through the house chatting away to Mum as the wet mud from her socks stained the carpet.

That night, Amy and I lay on my bed watching the Channel 4 festival coverage that Mum had videoed and reminisced about what an immense weekend we'd just experienced. Aside from the music, drinking and laughing, we also hadn't argued once during the whole weekend. We'd even managed a rare intimate moment in our rain battered tent one night. I think Amy was concerned that we might not make it out alive, so wanted to go out with one last moment of passion before the Grim Reaper reached his arm up out of the mud and took her. Such moments of intimacy had become a rarity since the Paris debacle and we were hurtling towards the "just good friends" stage of a relationship. But, in my mind at least, our mud stained Glasto lovemaking had given our relationship a boost and I was determined to keep it going.

To celebrate my 21st birthday, I'd bought Amy and I tickets to the V Festival in Chelmsford. Despite my protestations the previous year, V had returned and with Blur and The Prodigy headlining, and the likes of Beck and the Chemical Brothers on the bill, we were all set for another big weekend.

Somehow, my 16 year old sister persuaded Amy and my mum that she should be allowed to tag along. Amy and my sister had always got on well enough but what 21 year old wanted to go to a festival with his girlfriend and his kid sister? A couple of days before we headed to Chelmsford, Mum gave me almost the same talk she'd had with me before my first festival at Reading in 1992, but this time it was full of warnings about what to not let my sister do:

'Keep an eye on her at all times, don't let her smoke, don't let her have any more than 2 alcoholic drinks a day. If she even looks at a boy then make sure you put a stop to it. If you are going to get drunk then make sure Amy looks after her, she is a lovely responsible girl. I do wonder sometimes what she is doing going out with you.'

She went on to tell me that my Uncle Mick was also going to be there with my cousins. I knew that V was billing itself as a family friendly festival but this was getting ridiculous. I wanted to have a few drinks, watch bands, get involved with the late night partying and to end the night under canvas with my girlfriend, not go on a family outing.

As it turned out, I was an absolute, complete and utter tosspot at that festival. From the moment we arrived on site and Amy and my sister didn't want to head immediately to the bar area the second we'd pitched our tents. I was annoyed and went into grumpy toddler mode.

V had a system for buying alcohol where you had to queue up and buy tokens which you then exchanged at the bar for your drinks. On the Saturday lunchtime I decided that, in order to avoid queuing up again, I would buy enough in one transaction to keep the 3 of us drinking for the next two days.

I drank my way back into a good mood that afternoon, helped by the ever impeccable Teenage Fanclub and then James playing cracking sets on the Main Stage. Things began to darken when I went to the bar in the early evening. Stood in the queue, I looked at my beer tokens for the first time and saw that they had "SATURDAY ONLY" stamped on them. When I got to the front of the queue, the bar staff confirmed my worst fears that they could indeed only be used that day and that no refunds were given on unused tokens. I demanded to see the bar manager who reiterated the no refund policy. Never one to accept the wasting of money or beer, my inner Liam Gallagher came up with what seemed a simple solution. We would just have to drink all of the tokens that evening. By that time, my sister was already a pint over her daily limit, so it was down to Amy and I to get through the 10 "Saturday" tokens that I had left. I explained the potential 5 pints each or 6 pints/4 pints scenarios to Amy who just rolled her eyes.

Inexplicably, after only a couple more drinks, Amy announced that she, 'didn't really fancy any more.' I was apoplectic but, rather than cause a scene in front of 50,000 people, I marched off in the direction of the bar, muttering; "Fine, I'll find someone else to drink with". I didn't find anyone else to drink with, as that would have involved talking to strangers. I sat at the back of the field watching that nights headliners, Blur, and drank myself into a horrible mess, a really horrible mess. I sang along with gusto to Albarn and co as they blasted through 'Popscene' and 'Country Sad Ballad Man'. I even attempted to get up and dance to 'Song 2' before the deadly combination of alcohol and gravity saw me tumble into the back of a couple who were enjoying a light petting session.

Despite throwing lager down my neck, I still had 2 tokens left when the bar closed, which didn't improve my mood at all.

As Blur finished their set and the crowds headed back to their campsites, I made a valiant attempt to do the same. The fact that neither my arms or legs were responding to the commands from my brain was a problem but I headed for the vague area that I thought our tents were located in. I fell over the guy ropes to the first tent I tried to manoeuvre around and, as my face smashed into the adjacent tent peg, I could do nothing other than laugh. Thanks to not managing to get my paralysed arms down to break my fall, blood was now flowing from my mouth and nose. In my bewildered state, I thought that my injury would make Amy feel sympathetic to my plight and would see her wrap me up in a big warm hug. As my bearings were scrambled by lager interference, I decided that the best thing to do was to shout Amy's name as I wandered through the rows of tents. After what seemed like a week of my shouting, her head popped up like a meerkat from inside a tent and she hollered "Jay, get over here NOW!" I'm pretty sure she then said "Honestly, I am fucking sick of dealing with him" to anyone within earshot. Upon reaching our 2 tent mini-campsite, Amy looked me up and down and said, in what I thought was a very brusque tone; "You're drunk."

As I stood swaying, with blood dribbling down my front, I decided to go with the humorous defensive plan:

Me - 'Not just a pretty face are you my love, your vision is sparkling as well. You are perfect all over, absolutely perfectly perfect. Where are we sleeping?'

Amy - 'Why have you got blood all over your face, did someone take offence to you being the most annoying prat at this festival and smack you one?'

Me - 'As if I'm annoying sweetheart... No, what happened was, in my rush to get back here to kiss you, I fell over a tent rope and hit my face on the ground.'

Amy - 'I knew you would spoil this weekend. You're pathetic, Jay, you really are.'

Me – 'Thanks for pointing that out, my love.'

Amy – 'Me and your sister will sleep in our tent, you can sleep in the other one.'

Me – 'Don't be stupid, I'm fine, I will just have a bottle of water and then I'll.....'

I didn't get to finish my sentence, as I stumbled into and over a guy rope and went spinning to the floor. Amy rolled her eyes so fiercely they almost fell out of her head and said, 'Look, we'll talk about you ruining the festival in the morning, but for now just go to sleep.'

Me – 'You do realise you sound like my mum not my girlfriend, right? You used to love having a few drinks with me but now you're a miserable cow. I know what, why don't you go and find a charming man from Cambridge, I bet they wouldn't act like this, they would be sat with you sipping champagne, listening to classical music, not bringing you to festivals and getting leathered. Wankers. Your Cambridge wankers can go fuck themselves.'

She didn't respond, her eyes were enough to tell me that she wishes she had never met me. As Amy went to close the tent, I reached in and grabbed our emergency bottle of vodka. As she padlocked it from the inside, I opened the vodka and knew that I only had myself to blame. I slumped onto the grass and began to glug from the bottle which was the cheapest, crappiest brand so tasted foul. I began to loudly sing The Stone Roses debut album, track by track, whilst playing air maracas until the darkness finally took over.

I awoke the next morning to find my sister trying to drag me out of the puddle that I had slept in and into the tent.

My sister: 'C'mon Jay, get in this tent. Amy's still asleep, and you don't want her to see you in this mess. She's furious enough with you as it is. Are you trying to fuck up your relationship on purpose?'

Me : 'Don't swear.'

My sister: (laughing) 'Look at the bloody state of you and

what you did yesterday and you're having a go at me for swearing. Get in the tent you idiot.'

With one last push, I toppled inside and my 16 year old kid sister took off my muddy boots, put my glasses in their case and dried my hair with a towel, like I was a 2 year old kid who was incapable of doing it himself, before I passed out again.

When I regained consciousness a few hours later my tongue was stapled to the roof of my mouth and I felt like death. I quickly decided that the only way to quieten the banging noise in my head was to start drinking again, so a warm and hearty swig of rancid vodka was my breakfast. As I waited for the alcohol to flood my veins, I took a look around and found that Amy and my sister had, quite understandably, left me to my own devices. Amy had very kindly left me a note stuck to the side of my wellies, which said simply "See you at the usual place". At every festival I'd been to, the first thing I did was to establish such a place, a meeting point that all members of the group can always head to. If you got lost, or went to watch a band on your own, you always knew that at least some of the folks from the group would be residing back there. The best 'usual place' was normally in the Main Stage area, by an object that couldn't move, such as a tree or the bar. At Glastonbury in 1993, our place had been an ice cream van but the bloody thing kept moving, causing much confusion to our cider addled teenage brains.

I trundled off to the "usual place" which was a huge tree to the side of the stage in the Main Arena, stopping to get a veggie burger to line my stomach and a pint of cooking grade lager for each of us, which I thought would make Amy and my sister happy. It was 11.30am after all, and we were on holiday! Neither looked particularly ecstatic as I stumbled through the mainly seated crowd, spilling beer on random strangers as I struggled to keep hold of the paper pint pots.

They hardly spoke to me for the first hour. Luckily we

bumped into my Uncle Mick later in the afternoon, who cheered everyone up by gently taking the piss out of me and the 'bloody state' I was in. Slowly but surely the icy, perilous landscape between Amy and I began to thaw.

As the lager and rain flowed, the bands got gradually worse with Placebo, Apollo 440 and Fluke failing to hold anyone's attention on the V Stage. In the early evening lull, as we waited for Beck to reinvigorate the drenched masses, Amy and my sister decided to go back to the tent and change out of their drenched clothes. When they returned 20 minutes later, without having brought the bottle of vodka as I had politely requested, Amy informed me that all of her clothes were damp so she was wearing my Pepe jeans and Morrissey t-shirt. This meant that she was clad in my only set of clean and dry clothes. If I'd been sober I would have been annoyed. As it was I just kept drinking. It seemed like the only sensible course of action. I had a good jump around to Beck. A few months previously we had been so in love watching him, but this time she resisted all my attempts at a smooch or a dance. After he'd finished we stood in the rain, looking in other directions to avoid making eye contact, and didn't say a word.

I wandered off to the bar as the sun began to set and got lost coming back from the toilet prior to The Prodigy as, in the descending darkness, I could no longer find the "usual place". The Prod were scarily captivating as usual and during their set I befriended a group of Essex wideboys who insisted that I shared their spliff.

After politely declining their offer of continuing the night in the fleshpots of Chelmsford, I wandered back to our campsite, happy that I'd had a cracking day out. By the time I had stumbled back to the tents, ours was padlocked shut with Amy and my sister inside. They both pretended to be asleep when I banged on the canvas, so I sat in the small tent, stripped to my pants and finished the vodka.

The next morning Amy appeared to have forgiven me for being a prat, but she may have just decided to give up on me. I had punched another hole in the tapestry of our relationship.

I went home and shaved my head into a suedehead style in an attempt to cheer myself up. It didn't work. Instead, with my "Meat Is Murder" t-shirt on and this new hairstyle, I looked like an unhinged devotee of the Cult of Morrissey. Which is exactly what I was. Amy, with predictable disdain, hated it and initially refused to see me until, 'Your hair's grown a bit and you stop looking like a 1970's football hooligan'.

She relented to attend my celebratory 21st birthday dinner at our local Beefeater a couple of weeks later, where she was all painted on smiles to my parents and then the ice queen to me.

After the double whammy of my behaviour at V and new haircut, Amy didn't want to complete our summer festival hat-trick by joining me at Reading. She decided instead to go and spend a week volunteering for the National Trust, rebuilding old walls in Cornwall. She did ask me to go with her but I think that was more out of a sense of duty rather than actually wanting me to go. I curtly dismissed the idea as I was determined to reach my aim of going to 3 festivals in one summer. In the spring, Amy had suggested that we didn't go to any festivals that summer and instead should save up and go away on holiday together. Oh how I laughed at such an idea.

Amy set off for Cornwall to spend a week doing something worthwhile and I headed to Reading with Lou and her cockney mates. I had free reign to do whatever I wanted, with no girlfriend or sister to cast disparaging glances in my direction. Ironically, I didn't drink anywhere near as much as I had at V and didn't make a complete tit of myself either. Instead, I spent a lot of time on my own wandering the festival site, watching bands and thinking. Bands wise, it wasn't a classic line-up but Suede, Super Furry Animals and Stereophonics were all on festival-friendly form. I spent whole afternoons watching crap bands and picking over my relationship with Amy, wondering why it was all falling apart and whether I had the heart or maturity to save it. The only thing I worked out for sure was that I had no clue what to do next, other than get a drink and settle down to watch Mogwai unleash their sonic experiments on an unsuspecting Melody Maker tent crowd.

I also made twice daily visits to the Samaritans tent. They now offered a far more extensive menu than when I had first visited them at Reading 1992 and I would feast on tomato soup and a crusty roll for 60p, for both lunch and tea. A couple of times I was tempted to sit down and have a chat but even I had the self-awareness to realise that my relationship woes paled into insignificance when placed next to the comedowns that they were helping some of my fellow festival goers work through.

The set that everyone wanted to see was the reformed The Verve. They had blasted back into life with the swaggering rock 'n' roll of "Bittersweet Symphony". With Oasis championing Richard Ashcroft and dedicating "Cast No Shadow" to him, it felt like the world was theirs to claim. The festival organisers had stupidly refused to move them from their original slot headlining the Melody Maker tent on the Sunday night, which had been booked long before their renaissance. As I made my way over to the tent after watching a genuinely terrifying but compelling performance by Marilyn Manson on the main stage, I could see thousands of folks pushing and shoving their way in to get within sight and sound of the band as they took to the stage. I went round the far side of the tent, which was normally the least populated area but even that was packed solid. Over the years I'd been in plenty of football and gig crowds that had packed out a venue and left you wondering how you would get out alive if there was an emergency. None of my previous experiences compared to the crowd shoehorned into every tiny pocket of space awaiting Ashcroft's coronation.

During the opening song a girl, directly in front of me, passed out due to a combination of the crush and the unbearable heat. We didn't notice until the end of the song when everyone put their hands in the air to applaud and she slumped to the ground. Thankfully an off duty nurse in a Radiohead t-shirt was on hand to give her some water and help her out into the fresh air. I had resorted to planting my arm at a 90 degree angle across my chest in order to enable me to breathe normally and, more importantly, to protect my pint. The Verve were exceptional that night but, to be honest, I was just happy to get out of the tent in one piece.

Reading always signalled the end of the festival season and the end of the summer. On the grim, hungover, train journey back home the morning after The Verve's resurrection, I sat and thought about the year that lay ahead. A dark, almost comedic, cloud descended as I contemplated my time at university coming to an end. Despite not always being full of joy during my time in Cardiff, the thought of it all finishing in 10 months' time brought me out in a cold sweat.

The major world event that year took place on 31st August. I got up as usual on that warm Sunday morning, took two paracetamol, cursed the fact that I hadn't got in from 5th Avenue until 3am thanks to Doody insisting we stayed until last orders and poured myself into the driver's seat of dad's car. On the way to pick Doody and Jacko up for my first ever round of golf, I switched on the radio to find that Radio 1 were playing the unmistakable sound of Pan Pipes. Assuming that they were having some kind of technical problem, I turned off the pedestrian twinklings and instead concentrated my focus on driving in a straight line.

It was only as Jacko and then, shortly afterwards, Doody, piled into the car that I noticed the lack of traffic on the roads. I tuned the radio to our local station to get a traffic update only to be greeted with a solemn news announcer telling us that

Princess Diana was dead. With a simple, to the point, reaction of; "Oh" coming from each of us, we turned the radio off as it was starting to get a bit depressing. We weren't being callous and all agreed that it was sad that she'd died, particularly as her kids were so young, but within 30 seconds we were back to talking about football and planning our day out.

Upon reaching a deserted golf course, we were approached by an ashen faced club steward;

'Are you sure you still want to play today, lads?'

Doody: 'Eh? Why wouldn't we?'

Steward: 'Haven't you heard the news?'

Me: 'About Diana? Yeah.'

Steward: 'And you still want to play golf?'

Three of us in harmonic unison: 'Yes mate.'

Unbeknown to us, as we spent the morning hacking our way round the golf course, the world had gone into collective grief mode.

Eventually we wandered back into the bar, with the lads taking the mickey out of me for taking a record breaking 8 putts on the 18th green. We were greeted by an almost deserted bar. As I attracted the barman's attention to order the drinks, I asked;

'Are you showing the football later?'

Barman: 'Football?'

Me: 'Yeah. Liverpool v Newcastle.'

Barman: 'That game's cancelled.'

Doody: 'Really, why's that?'

Barman: 'Have you not heard the news?'

Jacko: 'Why do people keep asking us that?'

Barman: 'Diana's dead.'

Me: 'Yeah we heard that this morning. We're sad and all that but what's that got to do with the football being cancelled?'

He went on to tell us, through barely concealed grief, that the football was cancelled out of respect to Diana and that the bar would be closing shortly for the same reason. We drank our pints, chatting and joking as normal, as the dark stares of the barman bounced off us. Finding no other pubs open on our way home we went back to our respective houses.

Later that night I wandered round to Shin's who had, very conveniently, just moved in around the corner from us with his girlfriend. Finding that the TV was full of coverage of the death scene and crying celebrities, we decided to watch a film and order a pizza. As Shin fed the video of "Escape to Victory" into the machine, I rang Perfect Pizza and ordered a Hawaiian and a Vegetarian Supreme.

Having not eaten since that morning, I was a heady mix of hunger and annoyance when the film ended before our pizza had arrived. When the doorbell eventually pinged, a full 2 hours after I'd made the order, I sprang up from the sofa and opened the door with a theatrical flourish:

'Did you get lost mate?'

Delivery Guy: 'Very busy tonight, very busy.'

Me: 'Really? On a Sunday?'

Delivery Guy: 'Have you not seen the news?'

Jeez, not this again.

Me: 'Funnily enough you're not the first person to ask me that today. Anyway not to worry, here's your £13.50, no tip I'm afraid as I could have made it quicker myself.'

As a long-standing vegetarian I had learnt that you always had to check your pizza whilst the delivery guy (or girl) was still stood at the door, in case they had made a mistake....

Me: 'I ordered a Hawaiian and a Vegetarian Supreme.'

Delivery Guy: checks his note, 'Yes.'

Me: 'Well you've given me a Hawaiian and some kind of Meat Feast.'

Delivery Guy: 'Can you not have that instead? I won't charge you any extra.'

Me: 'No mate, I can't. The reason I ordered a Vegetarian Supreme is that I don't eat meat.'

Delivery Guy: Now raising his voice in high pitched anguish: 'The People's Princess is dead and all you can worry about is meat on a pizza, what is wrong with you?'

I couldn't help but burst out laughing, whilst this guy broke down in tears on Shin's doorstep muttering, 'The People's Princess.' I gently took £6.50 out of his still open hand, put the meaty pizza down next to his moped and closed the door. It had been a funny old day.

It was on the car journey back to Cardiff with my dad in mid-September, as I watched the motorway fly by, that I realised that I'd become totally institutionalised to university life. I was addicted to the Amy, studying, gigs and pub lifestyle. She was the most important part of my life but I wasn't even sure if she loved me anymore. The thought of leaving that lifestyle without a plan as to how my life would be post-Cardiff sat at the back of my brain, churning away coldly like milk turning slowly, inevitably into butter.

Amy returned to Wales, full of positivity thanks to her time working for the National Trust. Her new outlook on life appeared to involve lots of studying, smiling and denying that we were in a relationship. I had hardly seen her all summer, Glasto and

V fest aside, as she was always "too busy with things" to see me. I would react to such snubs by sending her endless letters explaining that my love for her was stronger than ever and include the obligatory Morrissey/Smiths filled compilation tape. I tried to at least make her chuckle by writing 'The More You Ignore Me, The Closer I Get' on my arm in black marker pen, taking a photo of it and posting it to her. She replied two days later with a postcard of Moz (that I had given her) and on the back was:

'You will get ink poisoning writing on yourself. What a tragic death Moz would think that would be. You may even get a song dedicated to you for it!

X'

The worst part of Amy's new outlook was that she had taken to treating me like a friend, purposefully avoiding doing anything that involved just the two of us. It appeared that my plan to put things right wasn't going to be as easy to put into practice as I had thought. My one hope was that our new house would get me back into her good books.

Since Amys breakdown in our damp, slug-infested house, I had resolved to find us a decent place to live. We had decided to invite Nic to join our happy gang and move in with us. Nic was a lovely lad from the West Country, who was obsessed with films in the same way that I was with indie music. Neil and I had met him at the cinema, when he turned around to giggle at our childlike squeals of fear during the opening scene of "Scream". With Lou and Neil now a fully-fledged couple, we needed a house that had a lot of private space and 5 bedrooms. I had started the search in March, so we had the pick of the best available houses. With nobody willing to trust me to find a house after the previous years disaster, we went, as a group, to look at some absolute dives before deciding on a neat and tidy house in Coburn Street which had the distinct advantage of not having either damp or slugs.

We were all set for our final year in Cardiff. It was a city that I had fallen firmly in love with. A fast growing metropolis that was starting to wake up from the battering that Thatcher had given South Wales throughout the 1980's. With the Tiger Bay regeneration and a thriving, bustling city centre, it had become a place that people wanted to live in or visit. It also had some immense gig venues, from the pubs and clubs through to our SU Great Hall and St David's Hall, as well as the gigantic Cardiff International Arena. With Cardiff Castle and it's acres of lush parkland smack bang in the city centre and an abundance of record stores, including the legendary Spillers Records, I couldn't get enough of the place.

My problems all lay with the increasing bitterness of our relationship. After the first few days in our new house, I knew that we were in deep trouble. Something about Amy had changed. I couldn't put my finger on exactly what but something had definitely changed. Maybe she'd met someone on her working holiday? Maybe being away from me for a few weeks had convinced her that she didn't want or need our relationship anymore? I tried to tackle her about it over a drink but she was having none of it:

'I don't want to have any serious conversations this year, let's just enjoy ourselves. We're young, free and I am determined to be happy. It's up to you whether you join in or not?'

I had absolutely no idea what that meant? Had she been to some kind of spiritual retreat rather than to work with the National Trust? I decided to use my default setting when confused and be exceedingly petty;

'Errrr...we aren't free. I'm not free, you're not free, we're still a couple aren't we? Free? Have you met someone else? Is that you trying to tell me in your clever, subtle Cambridge way?'

Whilst appearing to be sucking on a lemon to combat the effects of the tear gas that I had just fired in her direction, she retorted with, 'Trust me Jay, when I finally find the courage to fall out of love with you and leave, I won't be subtle in telling you. I will hold a bloody party.'

We had done so much growing up together, shared so much joy, love and so many amazing times. The flipside was the ever growing list of tears, arguments and regrets. This is where we found ourselves in September 1997, with me accusing her of seeing someone else and her talking of leaving me. The sad thing was that, by then, most people thought we had already split up and were now just good friends. I think that even our housemates had started to assume that.

As the term wore on, we would still go out for the occasional meal, to the pub or to a gig as a couple, but all the chemistry between us had gone. We would drink and talk for hours about anything and everything other than the 2 topics we really needed to address:

1. We had stopped talking about the future. Back in the early days of our relationship, we had made grand and elaborate plans for our post-Cardiff future. Where we would live (Cambridge), what lifestyle we would lead (mainly based around holidays and going to gigs). Now, if anyone asked what our plans were, they were offered a mumbled, vague reply and a swift changing of the subject. I finally brought up the subject of our future as we ate a takeaway pizza, watching "Breakfast At Tiffany's" on VHS in her bed, one night in November. It seemed like the right moment as we were happy, relaxed and watching Amy's favourite film. Instead her response was short and heartbreakingly sensible:

'Look, we both know we've got a lot of things to sort out. We probably need to have a lot of rows, tears and make-up sex, who knows, maybe even split up eventually, but can we not do it now? Let's just get on with this year, support each other, be there for each other and then sort this whole mess out after our exams? I can't face spending the next 6 months breaking each other's hearts and seeing you moping around the house singing

Moz songs to yourself. I just want to get my degree sorted, then we can work it out.'

I didn't say anything. She hadn't asked me any questions or given me any options in her state of the union address, so I just carried on stuffing pizza into my mouth.

She was right, of course. While we were in Cardiff we needed each other for support. We were the other's safety blanket and our lives had become intertwined and interdependent on each other. For the first time though, one of us had mentioned the elephant in the room, the possibility that we might split up after we left university. I nodded along and agreed with her statement, mainly because I knew I didn't want to even think about the possibility of us splitting up.

2. We had stopped sleeping together. That wasn't a good sign for a couple in middle age, let alone for a couple where one was 20 and the other was 21. We didn't actually decide to stop having sex. It was never discussed or planned, it just seemed to happen that we went from every night, to once a week, to once a month, to only on birthdays or at festivals, in the space of two years. Over the course of the previous 6 months, we'd slept together less and less until we got to the stage where the end of the night was sealed with a quick hug and a, "see you in the morning". I was even struggling to call up the mental images of the contours of her body when alone in the dark of my room.

Poor old Nic had joined a house where Lou and Neil spent most of their time together locked in their rooms and Amy and I were becoming the most dysfunctional couple since Elton John and Kiki Dee. I wanted us to be Nick Cave and PJ Harvey whose dark, brooding relationship was driven through the centre of Cave (& The Bad Seeds) 'The Boatman's Call' album. I saw us, like them, as having a love so intense and difficult to control that we would eventually walk inevitably down the road signposted 'break up and gut wrenching, heart pulping pain' but for now, still had so much to live for, so many experiences to get on and make. I was attempting to grow my hair, from its summer crop into a long, lank and interesting Cave style but it was still only at the hairy tennis ball stage. I wanted to be Cave, to be able to sum up my feelings in a haunting ballad like 'Far From Me'. My logic was that if I could write songs like that, then Amy would fall back into wearing the comfy worn old slippers that was my love for her. I would spend whole days writing song lyrics in the park in the autumnal drizzle and in The Tavern drying off, chasing the illusion that such 6th form poetry would save our relationship. I was spurting out line after line, hour after hour, searching desperately for the answer. I never showed them to her. I knew they were awful and that my words, even when written in my blood as one song was, weren't going to save us.

The big, communal nights out of our first two years at university had disappeared by that winter. Instead Amy would be upstairs studying or out with her course mates, Lou and Neil would be out and about doing coupley things, while Nic and I sat in the living room watching Buffy The Vampire Slayer or The Simpsons. Often we would go the entire evening without seeing another one of our housemates, before heading off to our respective rooms at some ungodly hour, with a mumbled, 'See you tomorrow.'

It hit me just how far Amy and I had fallen when I didn't get my traditional invite to stay at her parents' house in the period between Christmas and New Year. For the previous 2 years, we'd enjoyed a perfect middle class family festive period with much eating, drinking and the playing of parlour games. Amy and I would walk the family dog around the snow covered fields that surrounded her village for hours at a time. Like some kind of modern day Waltons, we would then go home to sit with her parents and roast chestnuts on the open fire. Things had changed now, her parents obviously felt that I was fast heading for the door marked "exit" and didn't need to put up with my uncivilised, Peterborian ways over the festive period any longer. They doted on Amy as their youngest daughter and had, quite correctly, drawn a direct link between her bouts of unhappiness and my presence in her life. I imagine that previously, Amy had stuck up for me and insisted that I be invited to family occasions. Now, it appeared, she had given up fighting for me. I couldn't really blame her.

1998

The Light Is Fading

I SHOULD have taken the Christmas snub in a mature way, as a wake-up call and changed my behaviour. Instead I took it as an invitation to become ever more childish. I still loved her, I still wanted to make it all ok but I couldn't resist the chance to get some form of petty revenge. My chance came when I was, no doubt reluctantly, invited to her sister's wedding. Amy had sat me down in the pub, bought me a pint and a bag of honey roasted peanuts (which I knew meant that she was either splitting up with me or had some good news). She billed it as a lovely weekend away for us to relax and enjoy the wedding, which was taking place at a country house somewhere in Hertfordshire. When she confirmed the date of the happy event as Saturday 23rd May, I should have just smiled sweetly, taken a swig of my pint and told her how much I was looking forward to spending the weekend with her.

Instead, I looked her straight in the eyes and said in a breezy tone, 'Oh, I can't go if that's the date. England are playing Saudi Arabia in a friendly at Wembley that afternoon. I've promised the lads that I'll go to the game. I can't let them down, no way.'

I knew, as the words tumbled out of my mouth that I was being a petty, pitiful wanker but I couldn't stop myself. It was like that moment when you've got a stinking hangover and you convince yourself that if you be sick, you will feel much better. As your fingers hit the back of your throat you panic and know you have done the wrong thing, but it's too late by then, the bile is on its way. I scrambled to stuff the words back into my mouth but they were out there, splattered on the floor.

I wanted her to react, to laugh, cry, hit me. She didn't make a scene though, she lent in close to me and for a split second I thought she was going to kiss me and say:

'I love it when you're mean, now take me home and ravage me.'

Instead she put her mouth so close to my ear that I could feel the acid dripping in her breath as she simply spat; 'Pathetic.'

She got up from her seat, grabbed her coat and made a point of slamming the pub door as she left. I turned to the assorted clientele, who were now all staring at me and said: 'No idea what's up with her, I only wanted to stay for another pint.' I stayed for more than one and wrapped my cosy beer fuelled melancholy hood over my head. She didn't come home that night. I'd waited up, wanting to give her the compilation tape I had made especially to commemorate our argument, a C90 tape filled with The Smiths "I Know It's Over" repeated 15 times. I stayed awake until 3am, before sleep won out in its battle against my petty desire for revenge.

It was only when I woke later that morning and realised that she still wasn't home, that it occurred to me that I was more concerned with giving her the tape than I was about whether she was ok or where she had spent the night.

We'd memorised each other's timetable, so I knew that she knew that I had a 9am lecture that morning. I figured that she would wait until I had headed out to come home. I was far better at this game than her though, and sat waiting at the kitchen table for her to return. Sure enough, at 9.15am, she came through the door, where she found her smirking boyfriend walking towards her and handing over a cassette. I smelt the unmistakable odour mix of cigarette smoke and male student bedroom on her clothes but stayed strong and silent. She looked at me slightly bemused as I walked into my room and shut the door.

With an exaggerated exhalation of breath she wandered up our winding staircase and into her room. Due to the creaking floorboards and worn carpet, I could hear her put the tape into her stereo. After realising what the song was, she hit fast forward and listened again. She repeated this for about 10 more hits of the fast forward button. Eventually she picked the tape out of its tray, threw it onto the floor and stamped on it for so long that I was convinced her leg was going to come through the ceiling.

When I had heard nothing more for about 20 minutes I went into the shower. Upon my return I found a note on my bed, written in her angriest scrawl:

"Jay, If you want us to be over just say so. Don't get Morrissey to do your dirty work. Surely I am worth more than that?

Ps - I could tell by the look on your face this morning you think I got off with someone last night, well I didn't. I got drunk and bored the girls from my course by saying how much I hate you and love you at the same time. I crashed at Bethan's. Check with her if you want."

I'd managed to finish on a magnificent double, I'd hurt her and made myself feel like a complete arsehole. I had also, once again, failed to spark the argument that I hoped would enable us to get all of our issues out in the open and find a way to put right all that was wrong between us. I had become the 21 year old equivalent of the boy in the playground who pulls the hair of the girl that he fancies just to get her to notice him. She was right, I was pathetic.

In an attempt to at least get back to being civil, I met her outside her mid morning lecture and we went for lunch at Bella Pasta. Amy spent the time reiterating her stance that we needed to: "concentrate on our exams" and "leave sorting out our relationship until we have both got our degrees". I just sat there daydreaming about how we had once been so passionately in love that we never got to the dessert menu when we had a meal. Even though it was only lunchtime, for this meal we had starter, main, desert and coffee. As a couple we had nowhere that we needed to be any more. We had gone from being a pair of lithe teenagers who would burn off any excess calories between the sheets to this podgy twenty something pairing who would comfort eat to hide their sadness.

That meal, both in the quality of the food and conversation was a new low for us. It was no fun, no silly in-jokes and the only smiling she did was at the waiter. It was excruciating to be part of a loveless conversation in a lifeless restaurant. She spoke in such a cold, businesslike manner that, at the end of the meal, I expected her to give me a print out of all that had been discussed for my records. Once again, I reluctantly agreed that we would "concentrate on our exams", and this time knew that I had to keep to it, for her sake if not my own. One more argument was all this relationship had in it and I wasn't going to waste it. Instead, as Amy went off shopping alone, I went home and did the only thing I knew could help me when faced with a crisis. I put "Vauxhall & I" on the stereo and turned off the light.

When Amy came home later that evening, having been for a drink with her coursemates, she found me still listening to Morrissey. With a glowing face that came from at least 5 vodka and slimlines, she decided to give me some invaluable advice:

'Honestly Jay, I think if you met Morrissey, you'd even manage to depress him.'

Pause to laugh at her own joke

'Remember when we first met and you would prattle on

for hours about how people were wrong when they said he was depressing. That, in fact, he was a very funny guy if you just listened properly to the lyrics? Now, look at you, sat here listening to "Strangeways Here We Bum" and thinking "Ohhhhh woe is me, my girlfriend thinks I'm a self-centred prat and I know she's right.

You should blame him you know, blame him for this mess that you've created for us. All those years sat listening to this turgid crap has turned your brain into mush, you're like a soddin' Morrissey zombie.'

Now warming to the theme, she wanders into the centre of my room and, to express her point, waves a flailing arm in the direction of my wall of Moz posters.

'Go on, blame him, it will mean you can totally rid yourself of any bad feelings, of any blame for the mess you've made of our relationship. Go on, just blame Morrissey for the crap you are making of your life. They will end up writing that on your gravestone. Here lies Jay – he blamed Morrissey."

Me – 'It's "Vauxhall & I".'

Amy – 'What?'

Me – 'I'm not listening to "Strangeways…." it's "Vauxhall & I".'

Amy –'The case for the prosecution rests your honour. I hope that the defendant putting me right on what album he is mentally wanking to is the final point that convinces the jury to find him guilty of being the shitest boyfriend in the history of the world.

Sod it. I give up, you've beaten me, goodnight.'

I woke the next morning to find that she had stuck a photo of her and me, standing smiling in her parents garden, on my bedroom door and had drawn a speech bubble coming out of my mouth, with the words "I blame Morrissey" contained within it.

If previous form was anything to go by, I should've got up and planned some act of revenge. As it was, I chuckled at the photo, left it pinned to the door (for the rest of the year) and went to my lecture. She had broken the "Bella Pasta Truce" but I was in no mood to strike back. What was the point? We both knew where this was going to end up, but I didn't want it to get there yet and I was pretty sure that she didn't either.

I decided that the best and most noble course of action was to just stay out of her way. By March of 1998 we were edging ever closer to finishing our time at university. I took to spending my days in the library studying, in the park listening to The Smiths or going to the pub on my own. Despite the constant feeling of gaping emptiness, I was starting to enjoy being on my own, not thinking or worrying about anyone else. In fact, I managed to get to a stage when I wasn't even thinking or worrying about life. I was just existing. Even when I went to the pub, I wasn't getting down and drinking to forget my troubles, it was usually just to watch the football. I was already subconsciously beginning to take the first steps to getting over the pain of our break up, even though we were still, just about, together.

This time alone didn't always go well though and occasionally I would, without someone drinking alongside me to regulate my visits to the bar, get absolutely plastered. One cold spring evening spent slumped at the foot of Nye Bevan's statue was a particular low point. Still, the 50p that a passing valley-boy threw at my head with a cheery " I bet he's bloody English, that tramp fella", was enough to get a portion of chips in an attempt to sober up.

Alternatively, I would spend whole evenings in my room, listening to music. 1997 had seen the final death knell of Britpop, summed up in the overblown dirge that was Oasis 3rd album, "Be Here Now". 1998 felt like a clean start, the start of something fresh. Like the rest of the UK, Amy and I were swept away by the gentle coffee table dance music contained within Air's "Moon Safari" album. We would play it at least once a day, with particular focus on the gorgeous "All I Need". The only other thing that we could agree on was that Theaudience single, "A Pessimist Is Never Disappointed" was both a shimmering glory of a pop song and summed up my attitude to life in it's 3 and a half minutes.

Amy was spending more and more time back in Cambridge, seeming to my self obsessed feelings, that she was desperate to get away from me. That Cardiff spring remained firmly stuck in the icy blasts of winter and I would seek refuge in her luxuriously duveted bed when she was away. We had stopped almost all forms of affection so that was now the closest I got to her. Even our hugs had gone from being full of love and warmth to the kind of pitying embrace that you give someone at a funeral.

I wasn't looking for anyone else, the thought didn't even cross my mind. I knew that Amy had dabbled with other members of the student population. I'd guessed first of all, before one of her coursemates let it slip after one too many Bacardi and Diet Cokes at Popscene. Then one night I saw it for myself.

She had headed out early one evening for her weekly drink with her coursemates at The Tavern. We were long past the point of her inviting me along, but I persuaded Neil and Nic to come to our local pub for a pint and a game of cards. It was as the barman rang the bell for last orders that we made the half-cut decision to head to the local chinese takeaway, 'Wok U Like'. With the alcohol fuelled high spirits of a night out flowing through my legs, I decided to do something special for my erstwhile girlfriend. I would get a quarter of crispy duck, (not easy for a vegetarian to order that) then go and walk her home from The Tav'.

I set off on the 300 yard journey gaily swinging the poor butchered duck carcass in a plastic bag, looking forward to getting back into Amys good books with this act of affection. Even with a few drinks inside me, I should've known that something was wrong when I walked through the pub door and saw Lauren, Amy's new best friend, whose facial expression went from a smile to 'Oh shit' as she spotted me.

Lauren - walking towards me and waving her hands as if she was fighting off a swarm of bees - 'She's not here. She's gone with some of the others up to Clwb Ifor Bach'.

Me - 'And hello to you as well Lauren. Errrr, if she's gone, how come her jacket and bag are still on that seat?'

Lauren - 'She was drunk and must have forgotten them. You can take them home for her if you like?'

Me - 'But I bought her a Chinese....'

Lauren- Now using her anti-swarm hand actions to subtly point me towards the exit - 'She can eat it in the morning can't she, it'll be fine.'

Me - 'Sod it. Well ok, I'll have a quick pint and then go home.'

She went to say; 'No, don't....' but by then I'd turned towards the bar. As I took my first step, a couple deep in a passionate canoodle on the makeshift dancefloor caught my eye. I could see that he was giving the kiss his all, eyes closed for extra meaning, one hand on the back of her head, the other firmly grasping her bum. As they swayed around in their circle of desire, the strobe lighting caught the side of her face, illuminating the whole scene for full effect. As the barman, who was a lad on my course, said "Oh, sorry you had to see that mate, pint and a chaser is it?", I felt the bag of cremated waterfowl slide out of my hand and split open onto the pub floor. Duck sauce seeped onto my Adidas Gazelles as I stood transfixed, watching my girlfriend dance and kiss a lad that I had never seen before. I knew I had to do something but had no idea what. My stomach had fallen to my feet, my head was swimming and I gripped the bar like it was the referee holding up my battered frame at the end of a boxing match against Mike Tyson. I ordered a pint and stood stock still as I downed it then, as the song changed and with Primal Scream 'Rocks' filling the air, this hastily thrown together couple got on with grinding the hell out of each other's thighs.

It felt like the world was watching me watching my girlfriend getting her rocks off with a bloke who I now noticed was wearing a rugby shirt tucked firmly in to his jeans. Christ, was this how low we'd sunk? Amy was so unhappy that she was out snogging a rugger bugger in the middle of the Tavern?

As the song came to an end, Lauren couldn't take the tension of the situation any longer and felt compelled to go and point out that I was stood at the bar. I could tell from the way that Amy was squinting over in my direction that at some point during this night of debauchery she had lost one or possibly both of her contact lenses. My chance to leave was long gone. I had to wait to see how this scenario, which appeared to be based on my worst nightmare, was going to pan out.

It didn't end with drama, instead she staggered over and indignantly asked, 'What the hell are you doing here?' before telling me, 'I'm very drunk and I know I will regret that in the morning but right now I don't care. I'm going to Metros with this lot in a bit, you can come if you want.'

That was it, no explanation, no sorry, no tears, just advising me that she was going to Metros. I declined her kind offer by growling into her ear:

'Fuck you, I'm going home. Your dinner's on the floor.'

With a quick and, possibly unnecessary, flick of the V's to Lauren and a nodding acknowledgment of the smirk that the pub bouncer was giving me, I was out of there.

I went home, plugged my headphones into the stereo,

loaded: "Workers Playtime", "Vauxhall & I", "Ladies & Gentlemen...", "Dog Man Star" and "His 'n' Hers" into the 5 CD tray and hit 'random'. My stereo, as always, caught my emotion in its randomness and selected "The Wild Ones". I laid back and let the alcohol in my system slowly defeat the adrenaline and render me unconscious.

I was snapped back into the dark night by what sounded like a ten man punch-up taking place in our bathroom. I checked my Indiana Jones clock and it read: 4:09am. My first thought was 'Surely she isn't going to take the piss totally and bring her conquest back to our house', but further intent listening confirmed that Amy alone was making this wide variety of yelps and curses. Either he was taking her to heights of passion filled euphoria that I hadn't ever managed or she was in pain? I gave it a couple of minutes, to allow my hangover to properly kick in and fill my head full of cloying cotton wool, before deciding that she was in distress and that I had better go and see what was happening.

As I walked into the bathroom, I could see her jabbing her finger into her eye and yelping as her fingernails hit her cornea. She was trying to get her contact lenses out.

Me - 'What are you doing? You've not got any contact lenses in, have you?'

Amy - 'What? Oh it's you. My eyes hurt, get my lenses out. I can't get my lenses out.'

Me - 'They're not in, look one is up here on the sink and the other one you must have lost sometime during the night. Remember when I saw you earlier you were squinting because you didn't have a lens in?'

Amy - 'What? I didn't see you earlier.'

Ok ,so that's how we're going to play it then, is it?

Me - 'That doesn't matter but you've scratched your cornea

224

now. You don't have a lens in, I promise you.'

Amy - 'Shall I go to bed then?'

Me - 'Yeah, I reckon so. Here, take 2 paracetamol as your eye and hangover are going to hurt like hell in a couple of hours.'

I helped her back to her feet and she shuffled off towards the stairs.

Amy - 'I still love you.'

Me - 'The bloody stupid thing is, I know you do.'

Aside from me examining her eye with the help of a torch the next morning, we never talked about that night or that bloke again.

I still hoped beyond hope that something, anything, would happen and that she would realise that we should stay together. I would make her tapes, sing her songs, try to make her laugh but nothing worked like it used to. The spark of attraction had gone. Ever since V97 and my subsequent haircut, I'd known that she didn't fancy me any more. The way she looked at me had altered, going from undiluted love and affection to the way that you look at an injured bird laying in the gutter after it's been attacked by a cat; full of sympathy but not knowing what to do for the best. Should she attempt to care for me or stamp on my head to put me out of my misery?

Amy had hardly changed the way she looked from 1995 when I went to sleep dreaming of her to 1998 when I went to bed dreaming of when she would leave me. Her hair was a little longer maybe, her eyes a little more wrinkled, thanks to being continually screwed up in frustration at something I'd done.

I knew that I still fancied her because the widget in the pit of my stomach kept activating to show me that I wanted to be near her. The problem was, I didn't feel that chemically unhinged surge of heart flickering attraction anymore. Whether she was dressed up for a night out or slobbing around the house in her pyjama's, I had lost that sense of being happy to chop off my left hand just for the chance to kiss her. For both of us, those heady nights spent together in the winter of 1995, felt like a lifetime ago.

The light had gone out.

Unlike Amy, my appearance had changed radically during our relationship. When we first got together, I was a 9 stone, skinny indie kid who could eat and drink anything he liked thanks to playing a lot of football and even going for the occasional run. I had a floppy haircut, round John Lennon style glasses and a plethora of band t-shirts which passed for a wardrobe. I looked exactly what I was at the time, a 19 year old student going to study Social Policy. I was obsessed with Morrissey and Peterborough United but, in the first flush of our love affair, Amy found that "cute". She later admitted that, when we first got together, she thought that I would grow out of my twin obsessions. How wrong she was and she was now paying the price for that mistake in tears, tantrums and scratched corneas. That wasn't a badge of honour. I knew it was pathetic to devote so much of my life to Morrissey and Peterborough United but they were me. Without them I was pretty sure that I didn't add up to much.

By 1998, I weighed at least 3 stone more than when I arrived in Cardiff thanks to a standard student diet of pizza, pasta and beer. I had given up playing football, bar the odd game. I had the remnants of a suedehead haircut that was slowly being cultivated into a Nick Cave style. I'd bought some half horn rimmed glasses purely on the basis that Morrissey had worn an almost identical pair through the late 1980's. My obsessions were taking over my life. For example, no matter how late I was for a lecture or a meeting in the pub, I couldn't leave my room without first carefully selecting 2 tracks to listen to, one each from Morrissey and The Smiths. That would drive Amy crazy as she stood at the door waiting for the tracks to end. Often she would just give up and announce her departure with a good old fashioned slamming of the front door. My girlfriend had long ago given up on asking what I had planned for Saturday afternoons. She knew that I would be spending that time glued to the radio, desperately waiting for news of The Posh's game. If it was a particularly big game, I would ring home and get Mum to hold the phone up to the radio, which was tuned to the local station and had live commentary. I spent more on phone calls listening to Posh games in my final year at Cardiff than I spent on food. I would go up to Amy's room after the game had finished only to find that she had gone out for the afternoon without me even noticing.

She also had to contend with the fact that living in Wales had made my love for England grow tenfold. I had always been proud to be English but, before I went to live Wales, I was genuine when I filled in the box marked "British" on my passport application. As far as I was concerned, those of us that lived in the four nations of the UK were 'all in it together'. Living in Wales for 3 years though, where every social, political or sporting problem had a simple solution: "blame it on the English", ignited my inner little Englander. Watching my nations football matches on the TV in various Cardiff pubs, the place would always explode with unbridled joy if our opponents scored.

I'd never enjoyed playing or watching rugby but would watch in fascination as the Welshmen and women would go crazy, desperate to beat England in the annual 5 Nations tournament. For the 1998 fixture, our SU decided, in their infinite wisdom, to put up a big screen for the England v Wales match and charge people to come in, watch the game and have a can of Brains Skull Attack. I would probably have walked past the poster advertising the event and not thought anymore of it, until I noticed in small letters on the bottom: ".....home and away seating areas will be in operation". Home and away areas? In a hall? I had to see what this was all about, so went and bought us tickets.

Amy wasn't keen to be in a hall full of rugby fans as she didn't have any sense of national pride and was mystified why anyone cared about which team won a 'sports match', but she reluctantly agreed to come along with me.

As we entered the hall on the afternoon of the match, the wall of noise created by 500 students singing 'Land Of My Fathers' hit us full in the face. A sea of red Wales shirts greeted us, as the melody rose and fell in an already drunken crescendo as far as my steamed up glasses would allow me to see. A steward examined our tickets and, after taking one look at my England shirt, began to usher us to an area slap-bang in the middle of the already packed hall, that was clearly marked "England Fans Only". As the speakers filled the air with the pre-match renidition of "God Save The Queen", the booing and obscenities quickly drowned out the tune. I was in my element, howling out the words, my right hand clasped to the three lions on my chest, which just seemed to wind up my Welsh cousins even further. The adrenaline was coming up, pounding through my system like the best drug known to mankind. It made me feel invincible for 30 seconds, even as my fellow students, some of whom were coursemates and people I would consider friends were stood 10 yards away calling me an 'English wanker'. The anthem ended and all eyes went back to the big screen. I instinctively reached for Amy's now clammy hand and looked into her increasingly nervous eyes. She had no interest in sport and now, here she was, in this pen, in a darkened hall, surrounded on all 4 sides by Welsh fans who all appeared ready to offer any Englishman in the room as a human sacrifice to the Rugby Gods.

Amy: 'Did you really have to do that?'

Me: 'Do what?'

Amy: 'Wind them up by singing about the Queen. Did you see Cerys over there shouting at you? She's a good friend of mine and she was calling you the c word. You wound them up...'

Me: 'All I was doing was singing the national bloody anthem,'

The game kicked off and the noise inside the hall was incredible, with the vast majority of fans turning their attention towards supporting their team. Unfortunately, the knuckle-draggers amongst the Welsh supporters decided that they would be better entertained hurling their empty beer cans into the pen that now contained around 100 England fans. The anger and hatred towards us was apparent from their snarling faces, but they had seemingly failed to grasp the futility of attempting to throw an empty beer can 50 yards across a room in the dark and hoping to hit your target. I couldn't help but laugh, but Amy was becoming increasingly twitchy and asked; "Can we go at half-time? Let's get out of here..." For the remainder of the half, nobody seemed interested in the game on the screen. The English had become the new sporting focus, with the massed ranks of rabid Welsh fans, the women being more rabid than the men, screaming obscenities and throwing anything that came to hand at our pen.

Once the half-time whistle had blown, I realised that Amy had had quite enough and I gave her a nod that we both know meant: 'let's get out of here and go to the pub'. I told the nearest steward that we needed to leave and he radioed ahead to get his colleagues to clear a path through the baying hordes. As we walked the 50 yards towards the door, I held Amy close if she were a small child I was taking off the ghost train at the fair after she'd got scared halfway round, quietly assuring her that it would all be ok and that we would soon be laughing about this in the pub. We got to within 10 yards of the exit and safety when, a spikey haired gentleman with a dragon painted on his face, threw an unopened can of the aforementioned Skull Attack at me with as much force as his skinny arms could muster. I knew he was aiming at me, as he screamed "Fucking speccy English twat" as the can left his sweaty palm. I was holding Amy's hand as she walked closely behind me but, as the projectile headed towards me, my natural survival instinct kicked in and without thinking, I ducked. The can hit Amy smack in the face. As her legs buckled and blood flowed from her nose, I gathered her up, furiously apologising and raced for the exit. Thankfully, after the initial gush of blood and bruising, Amy recovered over a couple of beverages in The Tav'. I felt it only fair that I bought all of the drinks that afternoon. Whilst downing her second gin and tonic, Amy told me to stop apologising and that she didn't blame me, which was very noble of her. If the situation had been reversed, I would have blamed her for taking me to the bloody rugby match in the first place and then again for ducking. She was a much nicer person than I was.

Things weren't all bad between us during 1998 and, as always, our top nights out were at gigs. We would let loose, get drunk and bounce around next to each other. The best of those nights came during the Easter break when we went to see Ray Davies on his 'Storyteller' tour at Cambridge Corn Exchange. As he struck up the Kinks classic, 'Sunny Afternoon', we were up from out seats, jigging up and down and singing. We lost ourselves in the 90 minute set that he served up, forgetting all the ill feeling as we had a hug to 'Waterloo Sunset'. I stayed at her folks house that night but didn't make any attempt to sneak across the landing and into her room where she was snoring off the vodka.

Following our original conversation about her sister's wedding clashing with the England v Saudi Arabia game, it was a subject that we purposefully avoided for months. In early May, with the wedding only a couple of weeks away, we couldn't put off talking about it any longer. We sat on the floor of my room, during one of our exam revision sessions and had a chat. My logic was that Amy's sister didn't like me so why would she want me at her wedding? That wasn't me being paranoid, it was a fact. At a barbeque at their parents' house the previous summer, after one too many glasses of Pimms, she had drunkenly confided in me that the whole family thought I wasn't good enough for Amy and that they all hoped that she would come to her senses soon.

What would she care if I missed her wedding ceremony in order to go and watch England play, in a meaningless friendly admittedly, at Wembley? My plan was to go and watch the match, thus missing the wedding ceremony, before getting the train out to Hertfordshire in order to attend the evening reception. I thought this was a marvellous plan that suited everyone. I got to attend the match, Amys sister didn't have to see me during the important part of her special day and then we would all get to have a drink and a dance in the evening. I was convinced that the plan was a winner and would see Amy tell me that I was a genius for thinking up such a schedule of events. Instead, when I told Amy of my idea, she paused, gave me a look of utter disdain and ranted:

'If any normal person had come up with that, I would ask them if they were joking? Unfortunately I know you too well and I know, by the inane grin on your face, that you seriously think that is a good plan. You're not normal, seriously, not normal at all. I think you need mental help. Normal people wouldn't care if it was the World Cup final let alone a stupid friendly against South Korea, they would come to the wedding. It is JUST FOOTBALL, it's not important. Don't you get it? Glen Hoddling, or whatever his name is, couldn't care less if you're there. This is my only sister's wedding for Christ sake. You're not normal, you really aren't. How the hell did I end up with you Jay? If it's not Morrissey you put before me and our relationship, it's bloody Posh and now if neither of those have anything that can interfere in our lives, we have England playing soddin' South Korea to take their place.'

Me: 'It's Saudi Arabia.' (I decided to let the Glenn Hoddling/ Hoddle point go. I didn't want to make things worse).

Amy: 'What?'

Me: 'You said England we're playing South Korea. It's Saudi Arabia.'

Amy 'Is that all you have to say? After what I just said, all you have to say is (imitates a childish whiney voice) "It's not Saudi Arabia we're playing its South Korea.'

Me: 'See you've got it wrong again. The game's against Saudi Arabia not South Korea.'

At this point she bared her teeth and launched herself at me like a screaming banshee, pummelling her hands into the sides of my unguarded head. It was the first time in our relationship that I had driven her to such extremes and I sat there, fending off her blows, thinking, "Well, she kept getting the team wrong, I had to correct her didn't I?

After 30 seconds her anger was spent and instead morphed into tearful dejection.

'Just do what you want. I don't care anymore, I really don't. I don't give a shit about you or about us. If you want rid of me just say it rather than putting me through this torture."

I had struck another critical blow to our relationship with my hammerhead. My behaviour was shameful, especially as England only managed a 0-0 with South Korea, I mean Saudi Arabia.

We abandoned our joint exam revision sessions after the 'South Korea row'. She was so desperate to avoid me that we hardly spoke or saw each other for the next couple of weeks. We both used the excuse of our need to revise to explain away the fact that we appeared to be allergic to breathing the same air. I spent most of my time in the library revising, with my rucksack packed full of Morrissey CDs to feed into the snapping jaws of my Discman. I would happily spend 5 or 6 hours in there, revising, listening to Moz and people watching, before heading to the pub for a couple of pints on my own. I would then put Moz back on my Discman, pick up some chips on the way back to the house, go straight into my bedroom and sleep. I repeated this hectic schedule every day for 3 weeks, readying myself for the exams and staying out of Amy's way. I knew that she wanted to focus on her revision and I also knew that she was tired of arguing. In one sense I was being considerate by staying out of her way, on the other hand I was worried that she was going to just end our relationship at that point. I figured if she didn't see me she couldn't tell me it was over.

After the first week of exams was negotiated, with friendly "good lucks" exchanged between us beforehand and "how was it?" afterwards, we both headed for Cardiff train station on the Friday afternoon. We walked the mile from our house, talking only of exams that we had sat and those still to come. The double trunked elephant grasped both of our legs, refusing to let go as we similarly refused to let it enter our light and fluffy conversation. At the station, as I made my way to platform 3, she headed to platform 1 with no more than thin lips brushing against sucked in cheeks to show for a goodbye.

Last Of The Gang To Leave

AFTER her sister's wedding, Amy stayed in Cambridge for a few days to enjoy the unconditional love provided by her family and to prepare for her final couple of exams in a house where the windows didn't rattle in the wind. She came back with a smile on her face and an over exaggerated spring in her step. She looked like the girl that I'd fallen in love with when I spilt blood on her trainers in 1995. She explained that this revived sense of joy was due to a "beautiful wedding" and the fact that "my course is nearly over, and I can go home permanently to my family and friends". The first one was a fair point, the second hurt but was no less than I deserved.

I struggled more when she got back than when she'd been away. We tried studying together again that week, but my insistence on revising for 25 minutes then putting on some music and trying to persuade her to dance along with me didn't help convince her that such sessions were useful. She was stressing about the exams whereas I quite enjoyed the tension and adrenaline that they provoked. The pressure of the situation normally meant that I felt like Rocky going in to fight Ivan Drago in Rocky IV before each exam, strangely confident despite knowing that the odds were stacked against me. On at least one occasion, a classmate caught me humming "The Eye Of The Tiger" whilst waiting in the corridor before entering the exam hall.

When not revising, I would sit for hours in the pub nursing a pint of Skull Attack with Nick Cave on my Discman. I knew that Amy and I were both unhappy with our relationship but I had no intention of giving up on it. If we were going to be unhappy, we could bloody well be unhappy together, forever. I was pretty sure that she didn't hold the same defeatist attitude and would, at some point, give me the "old Spanish archer" (I had been learning cockney slang from Lou). I was also stressed about what I was going to do for a career. My grades were pretty good so staying on to do an MSc either at Cardiff or at another university was an option. I loved my subject, would happily have studied it for another year and the student routine of eat, drink, gigs was now fully ingrained as my lifestyle. However, the one thing I was desperate to do was to get back to my friends, family and football in my beloved home city. When I vocalised this to Amy one day, she spat her Nescafé all over the carpet and chuckled:

'Christ Jay, when we finish in Cardiff you're never going to leave Peterborough again are you?'

I considered that a loaded question so decided not to answer.

Despite my best efforts, Amy hadn't fallen for the charms of my home city. Aside from the memorable Maundy Thursday night out, on the rare occasions she did come to mine, we would venture up town and explore all that Peterborough had to offer. This mainly involved drinking in crap bars and then watching fights in the streets outside rubbish nightclubs. She was impressed by our cathedral, but even that image was tainted slightly when, walking through the gardens one Sunday afternoon, we stumbled across a homeless couple having frantic sex against one of the ancient headstones.

We both had our final exam on the last Friday afternoon of term. It was with a mixture of relief and a need to pee that I walked out of the hall after my paper had been collected. An hour later in The Tavern, as Amy ran towards me, she had a look of unbridled joy on her face and breathlessly exclaimed; "Thank God that's over, we can get drunk then go home". I knew she was excited because that was the first time I'd seen her run in the 3 years that I had known her. If she had said those words to me a couple of years previously I would have known that she meant "get drunk and go home together". I now knew that she meant, "get drunk and then go home to Cambridge". I pushed that depressing thought into the dark fog that had now managed to take over at least half of the space in my brain and got on with having a final night out. We laughed, joked, drank, stood arm in arm at the bar and reminisced about the good times. We talked to passing acquaintances from our courses, swapping addresses and promising to stay in touch, knowing full well that no letter would ever be sent.

At pub closing time we made the familiar 50 yard journey to the SU nightclub. We danced, drank some more and didn't leave each other's side. Gloriously drunk and hanging onto each other for dear life, with the threat of the imminent 2am closing time loitering in the air like a bad smell, the DJ played Oasis - 'Slide Away'. As we passed the final bottle of MD 20/20 between our lips we used it as an impromptu microphone to lovingly howl the lyrics at each other. They were words that we both adored, even if they now simply pricked a distant memory of a time when we actually meant them. Right there, right then, it was the greatest song ever written. As tears began to roll down her face, I knew it was time to go home. We had spent a memorable final evening in Cardiff together but we both knew there would be no sunshine or shining with each other on our horizon.

After a long, stumbling 500 yard journey from the SU to our house, I felt a long suppressed urge to kiss her, to kiss her like I used to, to be wrapped up in each other, not in the 'I've got a mouthful of sawdust so can't possibly part my lips' way that we had been kissing for the last year. For about 30 seconds the kissing was both mutual and looking promising. Then to extinguish any faint hopes of a romantic, passionate end to our time in Cardiff, Amy broke away. I was hoping she was about to whisper 'My room or yours?' but I knew what she was going to say next and she didn't disappoint:

'I'm really sorry but that's made me feel sick...'

I stood in the hallway and watched my girlfriend sprint to the bathroom and make it to the sink a split second before the MD 20/20 was reanimated. The moment had long gone, so I went and held her hair back before carrying her up the stairs. As I gently undressed her and put her into bed, I wondered if that would be the final time I would carry out such a duty. I had presumed she was now deep in her alcoholic coma but instead she said:

'You've got sick on your t-shirt", before passing out.

I lay on the end of her bed, looked back at the face of the only girl I'd ever really loved and cried myself to sleep.

The next morning, her mum and dad arrived at some ungodly hour, desperate to get their daughter away from the filth and the scum of student life. I had gone to sleep hoping that the joy of the previous evening would manifest itself in Amy, prompting her to wake up early in order to squeeze in one last hungover embrace before her parents whisked her away. The reality of the situation was far more cold and lacking in romance as she woke me to say goodbye before rushing out of the door with a vague "I'll call you in the week" ringing in my ears as the front door slammed shut. So that was it, the end of our 3 years in Cardiff together. It didn't end with a kiss, a hug or even a shared cuppa.

I went back to my room, put "The Queen Is Dead" on the stereo, drained the tea from my Morrissey "2 lumps please" mug, sat on the floor in my Peterborough United pyjama's, gazed out of the window that was adorned with my England flag and wondered if maybe I hadn't paid Amy enough attention lately.

Lou and Neil were collected by their respective parents later that morning which left just Nic and I in the house. I had purposefully told my dad not to come until the Sunday morning as I had mistakenly thought that we would all go out for a good drink on the Saturday to say goodbye. It appeared that I was sadly deluded.

Nic suggested we go and spend the afternoon at the cinema watching "Fear & Loathing in Las Vegas" for the 2nd time that week. I was in no mood for popcorn and overpriced Pepsi though. I wanted to go to the pub, drink pints of my old friend Skull Attack and feel sorry for myself. Nic grudgingly came along to the pub for a couple of halves before muttering about not wanting to go home the next morning with a hangover and heading back to our house for the final time.

I spent my last evening in Cardiff in exactly the same way I had started life in the city 3 years previously, sat on my own in a pub.

I never saw Nic again. When I woke the next morning he had already left to go back to Swindon. He left me a note stuck to the fridge that simply read; "See you mate, all the best". Fair play to Nic, none of the false "let's keep in touch" stuff from him. We didn't have each other's addresses so couldn't have written to each other even if we'd had the inclination.

Like all good dads wanting to bring their sons back to the family fold, mine set off from home at the crack of dawn and was banging on our front door at 8am. After the obligatory cup of tea and his moaning about me not packing my stuff away properly and the fact that I 'stunk of booze', we got on with loading the car with my worldly goods. I had a last look around the old place and got a bit sentimental. It wasn't anyone's dream house, the bathroom was freezing even in summer and the windows rattled when there was a breath of wind but, compared to our house the previous year, it was a palace. I locked the door for the final time, dropped the keys off with the landlord at his newsagents and that was that. I was no longer a student.

48 hours after leaving Wales, having not unpacked anything other than my stereo, I was back working at Pearl. It was exactly 4 years to the day since I had started work there. The difference being that when I'd started back then, I knew I was off to university and it was only ever going to be temporary. In 1998, I sat there on my first morning back in the office in my usual seat and realised that this was now my "proper" job. As I made my way to the vending machine to collect another cup of hot chocolate with a hint of tomato soup, I vowed not to let that thought get me down and instead concentrated on the fact that I only had to be at work for a couple of weeks before I got to achieve every schoolboy's dream. I was going to the World Cup. Admittedly every schoolboy's dream is to play in the World Cup and we were only travelling over to France to watch the England games, but it was the closest I was going to get to being involved in a major tournament.

Amy had long since given up on talking about us taking a summer holiday together, so I had agreed many months previously to be part of our little gang heading to France. Amy had gone on holiday with her parents soon after leaving Cardiff so, aside from a couple of phone calls, I hadn't heard from her before I set off to represent my country.

Our (Doody, Shin, Jacko and I) plan was to drive from Peterborough to Toulouse, via the Dover-Calais ferry, in Doody's battered old F Reg Ford Escort. Making an early start on a fresh June morning, we were driving along the A14 at 4am when we heard an ominous pinging noise coming from the roof of the car. The next thing we heard was a whooooosh, as our bags and the bungee cords that had been holding them to the roof rack went flying off the car and into the road. We had little choice but to pull over and, with the only light coming from the headlights of the HGV's hurtling along the road, run into the traffic and collect our luggage.

With everything safely recovered and lashed firmly back in place, we made the journey to Toulouse in a little over 24 hours. Our plan was to stay on the continent for a fortnight, see a couple of England games, for which we didn't have tickets and then head back to Peterborough just in time to watch England lift the trophy, on the big screen in our local pub.

However, much the same as with mine and Jacko's inter railing trip, we were seriously out with our budgeting. It became obvious within 48 hours of being in France that we would be heading back home after a week, skint. We managed to fit plenty into that week though, including:

The brakes in the car failing whilst attempting to negotiate my old stomping ground of the Place De La Concorde.

Paying £150 each, from a tout, to get into the stadium to watch England v Romania. Only to find that our tickets put us in the middle of the Romania fans who celebrated wildly as they beat us 2-1.

Getting teargased and baton-charged by the gendarmerie, after accidentally wandering into a full scale riot in Lille, when we were just trying to find a pub for a pint.

Sitting in a hotel room in Lille, with all the pubs shut due to the riot, as England beat Columbia 30 miles away in Lens, watching the game on a 12 inch portable TV.

Me managing to reverse Doody's car into a petrol pump, halfway up the Alps, causing the terrified owners of the station to come running out brandishing fire extinguishers, whilst my mates stood across the road wetting themselves.

Going to the World Cup with my best mates was the ideal remedy to leaving university and not having a clue what I was doing with my life.

I came back from France with 6 francs in my pocket, 29p left on my overdraft and a maxed out credit card. I didn't want much in life really, just enough money to go and watch Posh, buy some music, go to some gigs and to keep hold of my relationship with Amy. The first 3 would be solved by working overtime but Amy and I was a very different proposition.

A couple of days after my return, Amy called to finalise the plans for us to return to Cardiff the following week for our graduation ceremony. I had decided while I was away that I wouldn't bother attending. My parents didn't seem that interested, I was skint and my mildly twisted logic was imploring me to put university behind me and get on with life. It was easier not to go. Of course, being the selfish sod that I was, I had only thought about me. For Amy, it transpired, graduation was a big deal. I had a suspicion that she wanted it to be our last big event, an end point both for our time at university and our time as a couple. I wasn't about to make it easy for her to leave me by attending. During what ended up being a fraught and angry phone call, I blurted out:

'What do you care if I come to the graduation? We both know you're going to leave me soon anyway!'

Amy: 'No I'm not.'

Me: 'You're not going to leave me or you're just not going to do it soon?'

Amy: 'Grow up.'

Me: 'I wish I was as mature as you. You really are the most mature person that I have ever met.'

Amy: 'You're pathetic sometimes.'

Me: 'Only sometimes? Well that's an improvement on what you normally think of me. Look, I know I don't fit in with the life that you want from now on. I know I'm not good enough, or middle class enough, or smart enough, or good enough, or smart enough. So go on, just do it, just fucking leave me, put us both out of our misery.'

She slammed the phone down.

She went to the graduation and had a lovely time with her family and ex-coursemates. I knew she had a lovely time as she called me, roaring drunk on champagne, on the night of the ceremony. Why she wasted her partying time ringing to tell me what a wonderful time she was having, and how I was missing out on saying "goodbye to Cardiff, to our University", I had no idea.

One Day (But Surely Not Today)

I KNEW that it would happen. I knew that one day Amy would realise that she was better off without me. I knew that one day she would wake up and realise that she didn't want to be with me anymore. It was always "one day" in my mind though, I never imagined that day becoming reality. An actual day.

The day came in early September 1998, on an idyllic, warm afternoon. The kind of day that couples should spend in a pub garden, getting slowly and gloriously drunk while planning their holidays and deciding on their top 5 summer songs. They would then walk home arm in arm, before running up the stairs, giggling and tearing at each other's clothes. I suspected that Amy and I weren't going to have that kind of day, when she met me on the platform at Cambridge station and the first thing she said was "I'm not going to the pub". I hadn't said a word at this point.

Instead of the pub we went to a café. I had at least moved on in the boyfriend stakes from 7 years previously with Jo, and paid for Amy's coffee. She had to pay for the piece of carrot cake she wanted though, I wasn't made of money.

I sat down at the table and she didn't say a word for a full 30 seconds. A slow, creeping sense of dread was spreading through my body and I was suddenly desperate to get to the pub. I knew what was coming.

With my nerves jangling like a Johnny Marr guitar riff, I decided to neck my boiling hot coffee in an attempt to calm down. The combination of my coughing and gasping woke Amy from her stupor. She looked up at me with eyes that I had looked into a million times before and seen love and anger in roughly equal measure. Now her beautiful pale blue eyes looked grey and tired.

She reached her hand across the cracked white vinyl of the table and when I flatly ignored it, she said gently:

Amy – 'Jay, give me your hand.'

Me – 'No.'

Amy – 'Why not? Just give me your hand...please.'

Me – 'No, because in all of those rom-com films you watch, when one person sits at a table in a café and holds the other persons hand, it's always to deliver bad news. If you want to give me bad news, if you want to break my heart, go right ahead but I'm not behaving like Meg Ryan and Tom Hanks.'

Amy -'Jay please don't make this more difficult than it already is.'

Me - 'And stop saying my name as well. You're like my mum, you only use my name when I have done something wrong or it's bad news.'

Amy – (now exasperated) 'JAY!'

Me - 'You're shouting my name now. Is it going to be bad news and I've done something wrong? Can't we go to the pub? Bad news is so much easier to take with a pint on the table. If we go to The Boxers, they have some Morrissey on the jukebox as well. With a pint, good music and a packet of dry roasted peanuts, I can handle anything you can throw at me. I don't even like coffee or fancy cafés and that muck has burned my throat, so I need a pint to cool down. You can't give me bad news here, that would be cruel, and I know you're not cruel.'

Amy – now red faced due to a toxic mixture of pain and anger: 'JAY please....'

Me – 'Christ, you can't even do that one thing for me. We have been together for 3 years and you can't just come to the pub with me. You've changed Amy, you really have. You used to be so kind, gentle and caring and now you can't even come to the pub to give me the bad news.'

Amy – 'Jay, please just shut up.'

Me – 'That's 5 times now you've said my name in this conversation, have you got a stutter?'

Amy – with tears of frustration now burning her flushed red cheeks; 'After 3 years together, after all the fucking amazing and bloody awful times we have shared, are you determined to make this as horrible as possible for me?'

Me – 'Yes Amy, It would seem that I am. Right, I'm going to The Boxers, are you coming or not?'

She nodded slowly and, carrying the navy Fred Perry bag that I'd bought her for her birthday just 6 weeks previously, followed me out of the door and across the road to The Crown. Sensing that this might be our final pub visit as a couple, I did the honourable thing and went to buy the drinks, first stopping off to put "The More You Ignore Me, The Closer I Get" on the jukebox. I was dragging it out, we both knew that, but I didn't have anywhere better to go and hoped that if I held on long enough she might just give in and not leave me. It was worth a shot.

Amy had asked for a glass of wine, so I bought her a pint of cider to see if that would stretch things out a bit longer. It didn't, it just annoyed her a tiny bit more. I finally sat down and she began what felt like a well rehearsed speech:

'Jay, this isn't an easy thing to say...'

Me – 'Shit, I forgot the dry roasted peanuts, did you want some?'

Amy – 'Jay it's over. We are over. I'm leaving you.'

Silence

More silence

As Moz had finished singing, the only noise was the CD jukebox frantically searching for my next selection.

With 'Ten Storey Love Song' finally filling the void, I tried to think of the words that conveyed my utter desolation. Eventually, lacking inspiration as I sat and watched her wiping tears away, I forced out:

'I understood the first time, you didn't need to say it 3 different ways.'

Of course, we both bloody knew why. It was totally down to me, I had thrown away her love and now had nobody to blame but myself. I wasn't about to blame myself in front of her though. Classy to the end, I rediscovered my inner tosspot and continued with:

'I can't believe you are doing this to us! Why?'

She would have been quite within her rights to either burst out laughing or pour her pint over my head. Instead, with her tears now making small pools in her dimples which were on full display thanks to the pained smile on her face, she looked to the floor and we went back to maintaining an excruciating silence. A tension that was only broken by us both sniffling and "Love Will Tear Us Apart" by Joy Division completing my 3 songs for £1 stint on the jukebox.

'I'm having another pint and a chaser, do you want a short or something?'

Amy – 'No, I think I should go, I need to…'

Me – 'Fucking hell, you can't even stay and have a drink with me after breaking my heart. Somewhere better to be? Need to go and find someone better already? I bet he's got a trust

248

fund and wears a tie with red trousers and a jumper slung over his shoulders even when it's hot and drinks Pimms. I hate the toffee-nosed twat already and he doesn't even exist yet.'

She shook her head slowly for a few seconds before picking up her bag and softly saying; 'I will call you tomorrow.' Wiping tears from her cheek, she turned and shuffled out of the pub, just as Ian Curtis was completing his paean to lost love. I smiled wryly, or as wryly as you can when the sobbing has taken hold.

After finishing my pint, I went to the bar with my tear stained specs making seeing where I was walking pretty difficult. I sat back at the table with my refilled glass, gazing into space and stayed there for an hour, until someone put The Levellers on the jukebox, thus signalling that it was time for me to leave. As evening descended, I wandered the still sun drenched streets of Cambridge, back to the train station and headed home. I needed to get back to Peterborough, where I had people that cared about me, people that would lend me a shoulder to cry on and, in Doody's case, give me his stock advice; "It will all be ok mate".

Unfortunately, the first person that I came across when I got back to our house was my mum.

Mum – 'Jay, is that you?'

Me - 'Yeah, it's me.'

Mum – walking out of the living room to cast her eyes on me: 'Are you drunk?'

Me - 'Amy's left me.'

Mum - 'Left you where?'

Me – 'She's left me, dumped me, told me it's over between us.'

As my words hung in the air, I wondered for a second if she'd heard me. Then her hyperventilating informed me that she had definitely heard. Through anguished sobs, she comforted me by growling:

'I knew it, I knew you would drive that beautiful girl away. That lovely girl, you drove her away. I said you would, didn't I say that Kevin? KEVIN!"

Dad, who upon hearing his name being shouted had wandered in from the kitchen, understandably asked; "What's happening?"

Mum – "Amy has left your son, that's what. She couldn't put up with his miserable, moaning, meanness anymore."

Me – "Eh? I didn't say any of that....."

Dad – like the Father from a bad 1970's sitcom, announced; "I'll be in the garage if anyone needs me..." and quickly walked away, offering me nothing more than a consoling pat on the shoulder.

I walked up the stairs, leaving Mum in a crumpled heap on the bottom step. I could still hear her sobbing as I laid on my bed and watched old episodes of Porridge on video before drifting into a dreamless sleep.

As the clock reached 6am, I woke up and had 5 glorious seconds where I'd forgotten about the events of the previous day and felt that life was sweet(ish), before reality hit home. I laid there for an hour with my ever trusty friend "Vauxhall & I" on the Discman, hoping that the day would just pass me by. I stayed there until Dad wandered in with a cup of tea to bluntly remind me that:

'Just because your girlfriend's left you, it doesn't mean you can have a day off work. Come on, get up and get on with it.'

I went to work in a blank eyed daze and sat for 8 hours completing my mundane set of tasks whilst grunting occasional pleasantries to my workmates. That was my routine for the next week.

When I wasn't at work, I sought solace with Morrissey. I would wallow for hours at a time and at weekends for whole days. I didn't want to eat, go out, do anything but listen to Moz and miss Amy. I was determined to wear my heartbreak as a badge of honour. He had everything that I required within the albums that had defined the last 5 years of my life. I didn't see the humour in his words anymore, just the seeping pain of crushed love in songs like "Seasick, Yet Still Docked", "Jack The Ripper" and, most poignantly, "Speedway".' He was my counsellor, my friend at the end of a set of headphones and all that I needed in order to sink ever lower in my own estimations.

This was me, a broken young man who would never find love again.

Over the course of the next fortnight, Amy and I would talk a lot on the phone, usually with me ringing in tears, or close to it. We played the endlessly futile game of me asking "Why?, What can I do? I will change, I promise", with her replying "It's not you, it's me, it's not your fault". I would go, on my own, to the pub after work and call her from the nearest phone box. I could hear the resignation in her voice as she realised it was me on the other end of the line. I would tell her repeatedly that I would change, that I would put her above Morrissey, above The Posh, that she would be my priority. She didn't believe what I was saying any more than I did.

As distinguished as Morrissey was at providing balm to the chapped lips of my heartbreak, I also sought periods of solace with "Seamonsters" by The Wedding Present. I played it every day as summer became autumn, whilst taking refuge in the space under my desk in our spare room. It was an album that had quiet moments that would explode in an instant into ravaged guitar noise that could blow a hole in your eardrum if you didn't get to the volume dial in time. This, coupled with some intense lyrics from Gedge, ticked all the boxes for my heartbreak. I don't think it was written as a concept album but, for me it told the story of a couple battered by love and the mistakes they'd made. From the glorious opening track, "Dalliance", through the look back at lost youth that was "Corduroy" to the desolate heart-shredding scene depicted in "Heather". It could move me to tears and then make me wildly jerk around the room screaming along to the words. I bloody loved that album. I would go to sleep listening to it, with Gedge growling away about betrayal and lost love as Amy invaded my dreamscape for yet another night.

I decided that Amy needed to hear it, to know exactly how I felt. I taped it for her and posted it with a note that simply read; "This album sums up how I feel…."

She wrote back a few days later with:

"No wonder you are depressed listening to that rubbish. I got as far as the 2nd track, which seems to be about a bloke having an affair with a woman called Dani. Are you trying to tell me you are seeing someone else?

If you are seeing someone, it's your life, so go for it. I hope you end up being happy again! Like we used to be!!!!!

X"

My first thought wasn't, 'Oh no she's missed the point of me sending her the album', it was, "She hasn't listened to that bloody song properly". In the 2nd song on the album, "Dare", Dani is the protagonists' girlfriend, not the woman he is trying to tempt into bed. That annoyed me.

By the end of the month, Amy and I had reached an uneasy truce. We'd agreed to be "great friends" and that we "had been through too much to not always be mates". Being a man, I thought that the truce meant that it was only a matter of time before we got back together. She was very clear that she didn't want me to leave her life, so I figured that one day soon she would realise that we should be reunited and live happily ever after. This way of thinking meant that my mood improved dramatically. I stopped listening to music under my desk and went back to jumping around the room. I would listen to tracks like The Smiths "Never Had No One Ever" and gleefully think that the song no longer applied to me. At least it wouldn't in the next few weeks when Amy would have her epiphany and insist on us getting back together.

She had given me absolutely no encouragement to think this way but I was desperate. The reality of the situation was that things were going to get a lot worse before they got better.

On a slate grey Sunday afternoon in October, I went to visit Amy in Cambridge as part of our new truce. She wanted to prove to us both that we could sit down, have lunch together and be friends. In our determination not to talk about our relationship, we ended up in Pizza Express discussing every other subject known to mankind, including her asking for the first time ever how The Posh were doing "in the league thing they play in". At one point she mentioned that she really wanted to go on another National Trust working holiday that autumn but didn't have enough money. I seized on the opportunity to show her that I really had changed by immediately offering to lend her the £250 that she needed. She looked shocked, as it was the first time that I had ever offered to lend or give her more than a pound, before insisting that wasn't what she'd meant and that she didn't want to borrow money from me. I was pretty sure she was just being polite so, when she went up to pay the bill (we had gone Dutch), I snuck out to the cashpoint across the road and withdrew £250. I silently thanked my £4 an hour job for helping me win my girlfriend back. Lending her this money would wipe out the pain of the house full of slugs in Cardiff, the drunken V Festival and the Paris trip. As I placed the small bundle of notes on the table in front of her, she made some mumblings about not being able to accept it. I wasn't having any of it and even opened her bag in an attempt to force the money inside. After a moment's hesitation, as she looked into my maniacal eyes, she thanked me, gave me a hug for the first time in 47 days and promised to pay the money back "ASAP".

That evening, as we went our separate ways at Cambridge station, she hugged me tightly, ruffled the back of my hair, kissed me on the cheek and whispered into my ear; "You're an amazing friend, Jay. I don't know what I'd do without you". I skipped onto the train, thinking, "I won't be just your friend for long…" I bounded to my seat and was asleep before the train had even left the station, falling into my first contented rest for weeks.

I spent the next fortnight convinced that life was going my way again. Every day was just one closer to Amy coming back to me. I even decided that when we got back together I would offer to move to Cambridge. If she loved me she would turn down such a gallant offer as she knew I didn't like the place, but my offer would be the important thing. I even went as far as looking in our local paper at flats to rent in places like Huntingdon and St Ives, which were halfway between our respective home cities. Never let it be said that I was a man that couldn't compromise.

I just had to be patient and wait for her to come back to me.

A couple of days after she got back from the National Trust jolly-up, Amy rang and asked if I fancied meeting up for a coffee that weekend? This is it, I thought, she has been away and seen that other people don't compare to me and is now ready to give our relationship another try.

What actually happened was that she sat me down in The Boxers and well and truly burst my bubble. She explained, with an inconsiderate smile on her face, that on the holiday she had met, 'This guy who I really connected with.' Before I had even finished the first hearty glug of my pint in a bid to buy myself some time to figure how to react, she ploughed on like an out of control piece of farming machinery.

'We slept together....more than once.'

I really didn't need to know how many times they had done it but she seemed determined to tell me. She felt that I "had a right to know", that she was going to see him again and that he lived locally. Of course he bloody well did. My prophecy had been self-fulfilling. She had eventually managed to find a nice Cambridge gentleman to replace her Peterborough ruffian.

As I struggled to hold my emotions in check, all I could hear her saying, almost on repeat was; 'I just want to have some fun... I just want to have some fun".

With a voice that now resembled a bowl of half set jelly, I forced out;

'That's fine. I want to have fun too. It's all fine, really. It's really fine.'

It wasn't fine. I didn't want to go and have fun, not without her, ever again.

I stumbled up from my seat, seeking out my traditional escape route from such situations, the bar and the jukebox. Three songs for a quid, three songs to make a point. As I took our drinks back to the table, The Buzzcocks - "Ever Fallen In Love (With Someone You Shouldn't Have)" came booming out of the pub speakers.

'Great song choice! I didn't say I loved him, did I?'

'I was thinking more that I fell in love with someone I shouldn't have three years ago.'

That was a cheap shot which struck her almost visibly in the chest and I regretted it straight away.

We drank in silence, me forcing the cold yellow liquid down my throat in an attempt to get drunk in world record time. As I drained the last dregs of my pint, I got up and said, as I'd done a thousand times before; 'Same again, yeah?'

This time though, I got a new answer to that rhetorical question.

She glanced at her watch and without looking at me muttered;

'Errrrr... Don't get me another one, Jay, I'm really busy today and I have to be somewhere in ten minutes.'

I knew her well enough to realise the darting eyes and the nibbling of the knuckle on her right hand meant that she was going to meet her new bloke.

I had been petty, selfish and childish for the last year (at least), and sat there struggling to take in what was becoming of my life. I knew one thing for sure and that was that I didn't want to cause her any more pain and upset. So, despite the devil inside screaming at me to tell her, "I know where you're going", I said nothing. As we said our goodbyes with a stilted, awkward hug the likes of which you give to your 2nd cousin that you've meet for the first time at a family function, I knew she was desperate to get away.

The stupid, almost funny, thing was that she had arranged to meet her new fella in a pub less than 100 yards away. So, as I gazed wistfully after her as she walked out of the door, I saw her cross the road and head to The Heir Apparent. I should have finished my drink, chuckled dryly at the ridiculousness of the scene, walked back to the train station and got on with my life. I should have done that but I didn't.

I downed my pint, pulled on my headphones and left the pub. With the sound of "Seamonsters" filling my ears, I crept into a narrow alleyway, the likes of which Cambridge is full of, just opposite The Heir Apparent and, with a jolt to the heart, realised that I could see Amy and her new man sat at a table talking. I could see them but I knew that, thanks to my cunning positioning, they couldn't see me. I stood there in a daze with Gedge growling in my ears, watching them. She looked so happy as she laughed along to something he was saying. As she pushed her hair behind her left ear she looked just how I remembered her in 1995.

This was her life now, sharing a bottle of wine and a bowl of olives, in a fancy pub with someone who made her smile. Which, in fairness, seemed a much better option than I had been offering lately: a pint of cider and a packet of dry roasted peanuts in an old man's pub with someone who made her cry.

I would have stayed there all afternoon, if a woman in a mobility scooter hadn't come up behind me, rammed into the back of my legs and urged me to 'Move please, I've been shouting you but you were listening to your bloody headphones.' That broke the spell and realising that, to the authorities, it might look like I was stalking my ex-girlfriend, I walked down the alleyway, took the long route back to the station and home.

I spent the next couple of weeks listening to a lot of Morrissey and The Wedding Present whilst attempting to take stock of my life. I was living at home with my mum and dad, working as a temp at a life assurance firm, with a degree that wasn't even enabling me to get interviews for graduate schemes let alone actually gain employment. The only graduate scheme pre-interview I'd had was for HMV, where I proceeded to tell the assessor how they didn't give Morrissey/The Smiths albums enough space in their Peterborough store. On my assessment form, he wrote "Shows good product knowledge but gave little indication of his commitment to a career in retail". I wasn't asked back to the next stage of the selection process.

I didn't have any solutions to the emotional rut I had fallen into. Instead I concentrated on trying to be 'normal'. Like every other 22 year old I knew, I went to work during the week before going out on Friday and Saturday nights to get drunk in crap nightclubs with my mates. The difference between me and my peers was that they were getting smashed and talking to members of the opposite sex. I would find myself in the darkened corners of Rinaldos, clutching a warm, over-priced bottle of lager while newly formed couples ground their hips against each other to songs like "Everybody – Backstreets Back". Invariably it would get to 1am and, with a stomach full of lager and a head full of dreams of Amy; I would walk out of the club without telling my mates and walk the two miles home, often in the pouring rain. Me going 'missing in action' as Doody and Jacko would call it, infuriated them but I knew that if I'd told them I was planning to leave early, they would have bought me another beer and forced me to stay. As it was, the long walk home was my favourite part of the night. I was all alone, wandering through the deserted streets and that was excellent thinking time. Or if I I'd had one too many, I would sing out loud, usually Morrissey tunes, much to the bemusement of any tramps that were kipping down for the night around Cathedral Square.

Come Back To What You Know

IT was on an alcohol fuelled Saturday night in November that I bumped into Jess. I hadn't spoken to her since the day she'd pushed me over in the park. If I'd caught sight of her in the club that night I would have, not for the first time, avoided her and left as quickly as possible. The last thing I needed was an argument and a drink tipped over my head. As it was though, I turned around from the bar with 3 bottles of foaming Budweiser in my hands and bumped straight into her, spilling the contents all over her top. She looked up to see who had committed such a crime and I braced myself for impact. Instead, she burst out laughing. I said a silent thanks to a god I didn't believe in and began to apologise.

Me: 'Shit, Jess, I'm really sorry, here let me clear that up.'

Jess: 'Errrr, as great as it is to see you again Jay, I don't really think you should be trying to mop lager out of my cleavage with a tissue do you?'

Me: 'Shit, sorry. I didn't mean to...'

Jess: still laughing 'It's fine, it's fine. I was wondering why I'd never bumped into you since you left me in the park that day. I didn't expect to get a faceful of beer when I next saw you though. I imagined that I would be the one throwing the drinks! Don't just stand there gawping at my wet chest, get me a Moscow Mule and then you can apologise some more for the mess you made, tonight and back then.'

Me: 'Ok, sure, definitely, yeah.'

I quickly ordered her drink and went to find Doody and Jacko to give them their half full bottles. When I came back, having given my mates only a minimal explanation of where I was going, Jess was sat in a booth on her own.

I'd quickly worked out that she had changed a lot in the last 3 years and was now a confident, pretty young woman who was happy to laugh at her ex-boyfriend when he made a prat of himself in a club.

As I went to sit down, she moved in her seat and I flinched, expecting a slap at the very least, which again made her chuckle. We spent the rest of the night discussing how crap the club was, why we were both single and what music we were into. Basically anything and everything other than talk about us splitting up 3 and half years previously. She wanted to know if I was "still obsessed with Morrissey" and feigned shock that I was still wearing my jeans with turn-ups and hadn't shaved off my sideburns. We moved onto her laughing and telling me about our hatred of shit nightclubs and the drunken fumbles that she had experienced in that very booth. I had to say something though; I couldn't just ignore the 'You Broke My Heart' neon sign that in, my inebriated state, appeared to be sitting on top of her head. I blurted out:

'Sorry... You know, about before. I...well... well I don't know what to say really, just sorry.'

Jess: 'It's a bit late, but thanks. Look, let's just leave it in the past shall we?'

As the club lights went up at 2am, we were still sat talking and laughing. As we wandered off to find our own friends for the journey home, we reached a vague agreement to, 'see you back here next week.'

I still went to sleep that night, after treating myself to a

10" Cheese & Tomato thin crust from Perfect Pizza, thinking of Amy. I couldn't deny how good it had felt to talk to a woman who had made me smile, seemed to enjoy my company and wanted to see me again. I was also quite glad to have finally been able to clear the air with her and emerge without a black eye.

The following Saturday night we wandered into 5th Avenue at pub closing time and after a quick drink, I told Doody and Jacko that I was going to the upper level of the club to see Jess. They both rolled their eyes and started singing in unison, the Embrace song "Come Back To What You Know". With their "good luck" and "be careful" ringing in my ears I walked up the stairs, hoping that Jess would be there. I strolled confidently to the bar, caught sight of her talking to her mates and my heart fluttered. I hadn't been expecting that, but it was a welcome return of some kind of urge towards the opposite sex. I was trying to process that feeling revival as she bounded over and gave me a hug and a kiss on the cheek.

With a beaming grin and holding my hand she opened the chat with: 'I've got a spare top in my bag, just in case you pour a drink all over my tits again.'

Without thinking, the fluttering kicked in again and my gaze must have inadvertently darted towards her chest.

'Ha ha, this week you're checking out my cleavage even before you've thrown a drink at it.'

I went bright red with sexual charge and embarrassment but her laughter had broken the last thin layer of ice between us and we wandered off to a booth. We sat, talked, laughed and drank the night away in much the same way as we had done the previous week. I was so out of practice when it came to flirting that I wasn't sure whether that was what she was doing when she kept flicking her hair around or if she had developed a nervous tic. I resorted to my schoolboy style of flirting and poked fun at her at every opportunity in the hope that it would make her laugh. I complimented her on the fact that, due to the blistering heat in the club, her eye make up looked similar to Robert Smith of The Cure. Not a line that is generally a winner but she giggled, smacked me playfully on the arm and moved ever closer to me on the seat.

By 1am, she was virtually sat on my lap but still we just kept talking. Even as the DJ announced the dreaded "Erection Section" to end the night, we didn't move. By 1.30am, we weren't talking anymore, we were looking around, catching a glimpse of the other then looking away. I now wasn't sure if we were both too drunk to take this any further or too shy. It became excruciating in the end, as we slowly turned and twisted our necks, like two juvenile giraffe's, waiting for the other one to take the final step and lean in for the kiss. To anyone watching we must have looked like a pair of inebriated fools having a late night staring competition. Eventually, with the music about to end for the night, our neck muscles finally gave up and, as our faces clunked together, we kissed. Within seconds of this breakthrough the lights in the club went up and the flock were shepherded out by the bouncers, signalling the end of another Saturday night out.

As we strolled down the stairs and out into the surprisingly parky autumnal air, we arranged to meet the following Monday night. We then both quickly located our mates and crossed the warzone that was the square at the front of the club. Every week, at this time the young male gladiators attempted to rip each other's shirts off, to show how masculine they were to their drunken, heckling girlfriends who were busy holding their jackets. Some nights, the ladies couldn't resist getting involved and, in a blur of hair and cries of "Get off him, he's my MAN...", all hell would break lose. This was a dangerous place to hang about and we never did, always choosing to gather our clan together and head off to the local kebab shop Turkish Delight to escape the mayhem. Even ensconced in "Turkish" you could never consider yourself safe from the drunken Neanderthals that stalked the city centre after nightclub chucking out time. Fortunately, we always got on well with the gents that worked at Turkish and they were never afraid to lock the doors of the shop to keep out the goons.

We all made it home safely that night and, 48 hours later, I found myself back at 5th Avenue. Monday in Peterborough was a pretty popular night out thanks to 5th running an 80's night called "The Margaret Thatcher Experience" which was run by the effervescent local DJ, Paul Stainton. The basic premise was a night of 80's music, 80p entrance fee and lots of drinks at 80p each. Essentially it was an excuse to get drunk on a Monday night and only spend £10, including your late night takeaway. I got there bright and early to get a couple of drinks down my neck before Jess turned up. This was different to our being in the same club and chatting and drinking as we had done for the last couple of weeks. No matter which way you dressed it up, this was a date. I'd even bought a new maroon Fred Perry polo shirt for the occasion. Once Jess had wandered in and plonked herself down on the sofa next to me, I went to the bar. At those prices, even I recognised that it was a good idea to buy the drinks. We sat and talked, as we had done on our last couple of meetings about life, loves and ambitions. The difference this time was, that for at least part of the evening, the music was pretty good. Monday nights were the only time that I would dance in a nightclub and, thanks to the cheap booze Jess and I were enthusiastically consuming to quell our nerves, we spent all of the indie section of the night on the dancefloor. As we swayed along to "This Charming Man", I realised that I was actually enjoying myself with a woman other than Amy. I had been convinced that this wouldn't happen again but here I was dancing, singing and kissing, though not all at once.

I had no idea where this thing between us was going and blotted out any such thoughts as best I could. I knew that I was on a night out with a woman that I fancied, wasn't that enough? Judging by the number of times she had leant in to kiss me and grabbed the back of my hair (a little too tightly for my liking if I'm honest) she was feeling the same. Other people my age lived for the moment, so why not me for a change? Everyone from my mates to my mum had been telling me for years that "you think too much about things" so, here I was not thinking, living on the edge, well, closer to the edge at least.

With both of us living with our parents, any move towards doing what most 22 and 19 year olds think they are best at was going to be problematic. As our petting moved towards what they prescribed against on swimming pool signs, we agreed that we needed to leave the club and find somewhere private.

Even though my family were away on holiday in North Wales, I didn't contemplate us going back to our house. My mum had forensic skills that would make a CSI team blush at their incompetence and I really didn't need another lecture.

Instead, after a quick confirmation that we were both having the same carnal thoughts, we jumped in a taxi and went to the local budget hotel, Formule One. A hotel that charged just £19.99 for the night and, if you arrived after 7pm, you had to put your credit card into the machine fixed to the main entrance door, which then unlocked and gave you the number of your room and a code to get in. The Ritz it wasn't. Neither of us had ever been to such an establishment before but, on that particular night, filled with alcohol and lust fuelled bravery, it seemed like the best idea in the world. We were both young, free and single, what harm could it do?

The magical front door of the hotel responded to my Barclaycard and let us into this den of iniquity. As we wandered along the corridor, our faces illuminated by the harsh glow of strip lighting, all the bravado that we'd shown in the taxi quickly fell away.

As we took refuge in our desolate hotel room, Jess sat on the bed, while I pulled out the only chair in the room and sat at the desk that I'm sure nobody staying there had ever used. I cracked open the 2 cans of emergency lager that we had smuggled in. I could feel the alcohol following our confidence by flowing out of our bodies. We needed this can to help set the scene and reinvigorate our libidos.

Ten minutes later, after I had made a quick trip to the machine in reception that prevented two potentially becoming three, we were laid on the bed. This sweaty embrace suddenly didn't seem like the inspired idea it had when we got into the taxi. The beautiful, confident young woman and the cocky man in his 20's now resembled a Chuckle Brothers tribute act, as we went 'to me, to you' with hands that now appeared to lack opposable thumbs and brains that were refusing to even find first gear. With the Krypton Factoresque task completed, vaguely successfully, we laid back in an awkward tangle of limbs with only the animal sounds from the other rooms breaking the silence. The alcohol now long gone, the sober reality of what we had just done started to hit home. I should have made a joke, broken the tension, made it seem like it really was the "bit of fun" that we had discussed prior to entering this godforsaken place. I could feel Jess restlessly drifting to sleep and laid still, not wanting to wake her, wondering if it would make me even more of a scumbag if I just got up and left? I needed to get home. I felt guilty about sleeping with someone other than Amy. With a hangover, in that Soviet style hotel room, that was all that was going through my head. I needed to get out, to get home, to seek solace in Morrissey's words.

When Jess woke at 7am, we dressed without saying a word, her in the bathroom, me in the bedroom, desperate to hide every square inch of the naked flesh that we had shared a couple of hours previously. We stood, waiting for the other to say something. After a full two minutes of painful silence, I blurted out, 'Let's just go shall we? I'll pay for you to get a cab home.' As we left the hotel and almost sprinted the 100 yards to the safety of the taxi rank, my sense of guilt and shitness was already kicking in. As a parting gesture, we shared the kind of kiss where our lips resembled two magnets, an invisible force holding them apart, before she got into a waiting taxi. I passed a crumpled fiver through the window to pay the fare, and ran. I didn't look back to see if the cab had moved off, I just ran. I didn't stop until I had covered the 2 miles back to our house. I phoned work and explained that I wouldn't be in due to a 24 hour bug. With the house all to myself, I put "Vauxhall & I" on the stereo and collapsed onto my bed in a puddle of self-loathing.

After 5 hours of sleep I felt a lot better about the world. Why was I feeling guilty about sleeping with someone else? Amy and I had been split up for a couple of months and she had moved onto a new man. I had to get on with my life as well. I was just about to ring Jess to apologise for my running away and to see if she fancied meeting up for a drink that evening, when the phone rang:

I was halfway through "Hello...", when the primeval growl on the other end of the line took over the conversation.

'I know where you fucking live, you smart twat. I'll come 'round in a bit and smash your skull in, you smart-arsed university prick.'

By 'smart twat', I had recognised the voice as Jess's Dad. After he slammed the phone down, I stood shaking, petrified that this giant of a man was going to come round and kick my head in.

I quickly surveyed my options, which boiled down to either ringing the police or ringing Jacko. I didn't fancy explaining the whole scenario to the police so opted for Jacko, who I knew was skiving off work as well. He answered the phone on the 3rd ring and I explained the fraught situation:

'You need to get round to mine now, I slept with Jess and

now her dad has just rang to say he is going to kick my head in and is coming round now and he is massive, so you have to come here and help me fight him off. HURRY UP.'

Like any good mate would, Jacko ambled round on his bike about an hour later, moaning that he was missing Home & Away, not caring that I could have been slaughtered in the time between our phone call and his arrival.

I had already taken precautions and reached into my dads golf bag and handed him a 2 iron, whilst I kept a firm grip on the 3 wood. We sat on our front porch for hours, with Jacko sniggering about me being an idiot and us both jumping up in fear if a car came around the corner and into the cul-de-sac where we lived. By early evening we decided that he probably wasn't coming after all. Jacko wanted to get home for the teatime edition of Home and Away so we packed away the golf clubs and I went back into the house.

As night descended, I decided to utilise Mum and Dad's bed as a king-sized comfort blanket. I jumped out of my skin when the phone rang at 11pm. With a sense of foreboding, I slowly picked up the receiver and whispered 'Hello.....' For a couple of seconds, all I could hear was heavy breathing which I realised was my own and then, from the other end of the line, came:

'If I EVER hear of you so much as talking to my daughter again, you are a dead man. Dead. Goodbye.'

As the phone went dead, I felt a mixture of fear, relief that my ordeal appeared to be over and a strange desire to chuckle at the fact that he had been civilised enough to end with a goodbye.

I had been an arsehole to Jess, not once but twice. With that thought rattling round my head, I reacted the only way I knew how. I went back to listening to indie tunes whilst sitting under my desk. This may have been vaguely endearing when I was 13, now that I was 22 it just looked a bit sad. I would go to work, come home, put on "Meat is Murder" or "Your Arsenal", and feel sorry for myself. Why did all of my relationships end in such a mess? I even began to wonder if I wasn't totally blameless.

I still went out with Doody and Jacko on weekends. It wasn't a conscious decision or even a choice, it was just what we did. We were single lads in our early 20's living a couple of miles from the city centre. What else were we going to do? I always went out with the intention of not ending up in a crappy club but inevitability that's where I would find myself every Friday and Saturday night. It had now become traditional for me to enter such places with Doody and Jacko, have a couple of drinks then leave on my own after a couple of hours. I would occasionally leave even earlier than that, usually when I spotted Jess on the dancefloor. I didn't want to embarrass her or cause a scene. I also didn't want her dad to kick my head in.

It was in a taxi home, on a stormy November night, that I decided that I had better get off my arse and find a proper job. Pearl had been a useful temp job over the years but it was time for me to start thinking about the future, grow up, get a career and be a man. That was a depressing cab journey.

My first permanent job duly arrived later that month when I was the successful applicant for the vacant "Collections Officer" post at our local building society. My job was to telephone people who had fallen into arrears with their mortgage repayments and attempt to persuade them to pay up. In truth, my heart wasn't in the job and I wasn't very good at it. I would listen to what I considered to be genuine tales of woe and misfortune from our borrowers and mark on their file that they should be given another month to get themselves together. It was a difficult subject to talk to people about and anyone that burst into tears instantly got my sympathy and a promise of "we will do whatever we can to help". I was pretty sure this wasn't the approach my bosses wanted me to take. I thought that by making lots of calls and occasionally persuading some wealthy type who had genuinely forgotten to pay their mortgage to deposit cash into our account would mean that the bosses would leave me alone. Instead, I got a shock one day when our big departmental boss called me in to his office. He was a bear of a man with a temper to match. As he slid onto his high leather swivel chair and looked down at me in my plastic seat, which looked like it had been stolen from a local primary school, it was obvious I had done something wrong:

Him: 'Mr Jones, you have been with us now for a few weeks is that correct?'

Me: The obvious answer was, 'You know full well it's bloody correct', but what came out of my mouth was a meek; 'Yes that's right, sir.'

Him: 'Did you know we produce a report which shows me how much money you have collected each week from chasing debtors?'

Me: Nervous chuckle - 'No, I didn't know that.'

Him: 'Did you also know, and I'm sure you were told in your induction to the office, that we record all calls that you make.

Me: Mildly terrified chuckle - 'No, I didn't know that either.'

Him: 'Let me play you a recording of a call you made to a customer last week.'

As the sound of my voice filled the room, I realised that the call he was playing was to a man who gave me no real reason why he couldn't pay his mortgage but during our conversation, revealed that he was a Posh fan. As Big Boss and I sat and listened to 5 minutes of us discussing everything from Posh's current form to whether or not we needed a new striker, I felt my face going first red, then scarlet. I knew what was coming, as Big Boss turned up the volume on the speakers and gave me a steely eyed smirk. I brought the call to an end by saying cheerily:

'Look, you're only £3000 behind, I will just make a note on the system to say that you are trying to pay and to give you another couple of months. Nobody here will notice for a while. Anyway, what's a few more weeks going to hurt, I'm sure you'll pay it in the end.

Ok then mate. Yeah, good talking to you as well. Up The Posh.'

I wanted to burst out laughing as Big Boss and I sat there with the dialling tone buzzing in our ears. He didn't laugh though. He issued me with a final written warning. I had only been there for 3 weeks and hadn't had any other warnings, written or otherwise, but it didn't feel like the right time to argue with him over HR policy. I knew then that, although I needed to keep the job in order to continue to bank my salary of £12,500 a year, I also needed to get on with finding a position elsewhere.

My permanent employment and salary meant that Dad could get on with badgering me into doing the two things that, following my degree, he wanted me to do most in life. Namely buy a car and leave home (for good).

My buying of a car was born out of necessity that December. Since I'd started work back in Peterborough, my old mate Doods had been giving me a lift to work and back. This scenario worked out fine until I walked into his house one morning and asked:

Me 'Where's your car, Doods?'

Doods: 'In the usual place.'

Me: 'No it's not.'

Doods: 'Stop being a knob, it's freezing cold and I've got a blinding hangover.'

Me: 'Honestly mate, it's not in the usual place.'

Doods: 'If you're messing me about, Jay, I swear, I am going to batter you.'

We walked out to the usual place with me saying, 'It's not there, it's not there' to find that, as I had been saying, the car wasn't there. I resisted the temptation to say 'I told you.' Fortunately the police did find Doods car a week later, unfortunately it was after a boat had got stuck on its roof in the local river.

I bought my first car, an ageing Renault Clio, the following week with all the cash that I had in the world and my first bank loan. My dad was a picture of brooding delight as I handed over the money at the garage. I knew that he was thinking:

'No more living like a student for you my boy, this is the real world now. You can experience some of my life, with its bank loans and moaning about the price of car insurance.'

That Christmas was a strange time. I finally had a half decent job, a few quid in my pocket and was back home with my mates and my family. The problem was that I still had an Amy shaped hole in my life. I spent far more time thinking about her now that we were apart than I ever did when we were together. Maybe that was the problem neatly summed up right there.

I knew that I had to put our relationship behind me and get on with my life but I was enjoying playing the heartbroken, sensitive victim. It wasn't an act as such but it was a piece of Mozesque drama that suited my battered personality perfectly. My family and mates weren't enjoying my wallowing but I wasn't bothered. I got to sit in my room, listen to my music and feel that the words of Morrissey and Billy Bragg were full of meaning (for a self-centred tosspot).

I spent Christmas morning convinced that Amy would ring and say that she had made a terrible mistake and that we should get back together. I've no idea why I thought Christmas Day was going to provoke such a realisation in her but, by mid-afternoon, I'd grudgingly accepted that she wasn't going

271

to ring. I sat at the table for dinner, with a party hat perched wonkily on my head, desperate to get back upstairs, back to my music, while the festivities whirled around me.

1999

Moving On
(By Sitting in My Pants & Listening to Moz)

1999 opened miserably. I'd never been a fan of New Year's Eve, all those once a year revellers out cluttering up the streets, imploring everyone to have a great time. It was a Peterborough tradition to leave whichever crappy club you were in at 11.45pm and head to a freezing Cathedral Square. There, surrounded by other drunken revellers, we would celebrate the coming of the new year by hugging and kissing complete strangers. We had been doing the same thing for every NYE since 1992, but as 1998 became 1999, I'd had enough of this forced fun. I would happily have thrown myself off Town Bridge and into the River Nene rather than have to wish any more strangers "Happy New Year" or listen to the sound of Prince's "1999" being played in every bar and club on endless repeat. The rest of the world could party like it was 1999 if it wanted to, but I stood in the cold of Cathedral Square and daydreamed about being at home in bed with a cup of tea and a cheese sandwich, listening to "Strangeways Here We Come". In the end, that thought proved irresistible and I slipped away from the square at five to midnight. I saw in the New Year by walking home alone through the deserted city centre streets. That suited me just fine.

The early weeks of the year were alive with talk of how different the world would be in a years' time with the dawning of a new millennium. I wasn't excited, it would be just another year. As Morrissey stated: "The year 2000 won't change anything, someone will still need to work in Woolworths".

I wasn't interested in any of the new music that was being released, so spent my time and money buying old albums. It was during a trip to HMV in January, that I stumbled across Johnny Cash – "Live At Folsom Prison" on CD for just £5.99. I figured that for such a bargain price I was duty bound to buy it. I had known of Johnny Cash previously of course, but this album was to elevate him in my eyes to legendary status: right up there with The Charlatans, The Stone Roses and just below Morrissey and Billy Bragg. Folsom was the ultimate live album, a country minstrel singing songs of love, loss and wrongdoing to a room full of convicts. The crowd interaction and their joy at hearing the songs is stunning. When he opens the show with "Folsom Prison Blues", you can almost hear the prison guards shuffling nervously, not knowing whether Cash or the inmates were the bigger danger. The man was the ultimate crowd pleaser and that crowd on that day absolutely adored him. I would lay under my desk and howl along to the likes of "Cocaine Blues" and "Orange Blossom Special". It lifted my spirits and convinced me that I needed to get on with my life. Amy had gone but, with the whole world ahead of me or, at the very least, a city within which surely someone would fancy me in the darkened corners of a nightclub?

I made the trip to Cambridge in February to meet Amy for what was now becoming a regular lunch meeting. Before I'd had much of a chance to say anything, she blurted out that she was moving in with her new fella. I realised in that instant that she had started on her adult life while I was still spending hours wondering what my favourite track on "The Queen is Dead" was.

I knew that my lack of horror, grief or tears upon hearing

her news meant that I was finally ready to move on. As we walked along the river, I told her that I was over her, that I was moving on as well and that I hoped we could both be happy. I meant every word. I had loved her, in reality probably still loved her and really did want her to be happy. It was the first slice of maturity that I had served up in years. She made a face that, in all the time I'd known her, I hadn't seen her make before. It was somewhere between relief and sadness. Either that or she'd bitten her tongue.

Our hug goodbye that day was a little tighter than it had been for at least two years, as it dawned on us both that we would now inevitably drift apart. We vowed to stay friends but the reality was that life had different plans for us. I didn't have a master plan. I didn't have a plan at all but I knew I needed to stop looking back and start stumbling blindly forward.

On the train home I formulated a double-barrelled course of action, one of which was to start seeing someone new and the other was to move out of my parents' house. I wasn't planning on changing my personality and start chatting up women, so the first one would have to take care of itself eventually. The second one, though, I could put into practice.

I had first left home when I moved to Hereford and then Cardiff in 1995. I had gone away, grown up to a certain extent and came home after my time at university was over. It was tough for Mum and I to live back under the same roof. I had got used to living my life exactly the way that I wanted to. I wasn't happy to get tutted at or questioned every time I got a bottle of lager (that I'd bought) out of the fridge or starting World War III by taking the wrong size towel out of the airing cupboard. Mum had used the time that I was away to de-Jay her house and get it exactly how she wanted it. As much as she loved me, she was struggling with my rolling back into town and leaving toast crumbs all over her kitchen work tops. At a surprisingly calm dinner table discussion, Mum and I agreed that it was time for me to move out permanently.

Jacko was having much the same conversation with his mum, so we set about finding both a suitable house for us to move into and an extra housemate to help pay the bills. With Doody having already moved in with our mate Deano, that ruled him out. In the end, we decided to invite a lad we knew from football and nights out, called Ally, to move into the comfortable 3 bed semi-detached house that we had found to rent. I knew Jacko inside out thanks to our years of being mates, but living with Ally was an eye-opener. He was four years older than us but didn't appear to own anything in the world other than his clothes and a Tottenham Hotspur alarm clock. He took the box room as it was the cheapest and he didn't have anything to put in it.

We moved in at the end of March and it was revelation to have my own space again, living life how I wanted to. Not that I did anything rebellious or radical, but if I wanted to spend a Sunday sat in my pants, in bed, drinking tea and listening to Morrissey, I could. At times our house resembled a football dressing room, both in the number of lads that would be in it and the relentless mickey-taking that would take place. Weekends or weeknights, ours became the house that all our mates would head to before or after a night out. We had some funny old times, from me nearly burning the house down when leaving a pizza under the grill and falling into a drunken coma at 3am, through to our mate Gaz deciding that 5am on a Sunday morning was the ideal time to strip naked and play golf on our front lawn.

Even up in my room, I wasn't safe from visitors. I would occasionally attempt to sneak up there, turn off the lights, draw the curtains and relax with a bottle of lager and The Smiths. I never got the chance to wallow for long though, as one of the lads would wander up the stairs to the bathroom and barge into my room to ask; 'What the bloody hell are you doing up here on your own in the dark? Get downstairs and watch the second half of the football, man.'

The 3 of us, along with the majority of our mates, all played for the same Sunday league team. The games that we played and, most importantly, the days out in the pub after the final whistle were some of the funniest times of my life. Winning or losing football matches with your mates, helping each other out, whether that's defending a corner or defending each other in a 22 man brawl, the sense of camaraderie was life-affirming. It was a time when none of us had any responsibilities, unless you counted the need to get up for work on a Monday morning. Our pre-match plans would start with meeting in one of Peterborough's pubs on the Saturday night, party at Deano's or ours after nightclub chucking out time, crash out at 4am, up at 8.30am to play football and then de-camp to our local pub, The Whittle Way, as soon as we had showered after the game. We would stay there watching football, laughing and joking until we fell over. It was a simple but bloody fun way of living life.

Moving into the house, and the football days out had helped me put both Amy and Cardiff to the back of my mind, As winter eased into spring, we decided that the ideal summer holiday would be a trip to Bulgaria, to incorporate some time around the pool and take in the game England were playing in the capital. Despite our hotel being in Sunny Beach, some 225 miles from Sofia, we booked it knowing that somehow we would find transport to get us to and from the match. We were all in our early 20's, we didn't worry about such things. Of far more interest was that it was boiling hot, our hotel was on the beachfront and beer was only 30p a pint. We arrived and immediately hit it hard. On the first night, Deano and I ended up fully clothed in the sea and then on a tourist car-train that stopped mysteriously in the middle of some woods. As we were the only passengers and the driver, who looked very unhappy, was heading our way, we decided to run back into town despite appearing to be too drunk to stand. The lads were all delighted to see us when we returned.

Deano ended the night drinking his pint whilst sat in the

pool at 6am, despite the hotel staff insisting he would "die from chemical we put in pool". I'd slunk off to my room and redecorated the walls and floor of our bathroom. The rest of the holiday continued in much the same vein. I felt like a different person, like I had shrugged off the miserable git that I had been for far too long and was now prepared to put myself out there and enjoy what adventures life had to offer. Whether it was Doody spending a night asleep in the woods or 'Tommy' the hotel barman taking us to this strange open air nightclub in the hills surrounding the resort, where he insisted that no foreign tourists had ever been before, it was a mad old holiday.

On the day of the England game in Sofia, we paid £40 each to board a plane chartered by one of the local bar owners to take us to the capital. The plane journey from Stansted to Bulgaria had been my first so I was still a little nervous about flying, particularly as the bar owner laughed heartily when I asked him which airport we would be flying from. We were piled into an ancient bus, along with England fans from neighbouring hotels and driven out to a field in the middle of nowhere. There we set eyes on our plane. I hadn't seen anything like it since the last time I'd watched one of the Indiana Jones films. We stood there, open mouthed, looking at the dual propellers that were to power this 50 seater plane. None of us got onboard thinking we would ever see our hotel again, let alone the green and pleasant land that we called home.

Thankfully we made it to Sofia in one piece and had time for a few friendly drinks with the locals before watching England play out a decent 1-1 draw. The few beers that we had gulped down ensured that our plane was full of male bravado for the return trip to Sunny Beach. Whereas we had flown to Sofia in a stunned, worried silence, we flew back to laughter and lots of "I knew this plane would be fine, course I did, never a problem for me."

We returned to England 48 hours later, with tales to tell and smiles on our faces. I couldn't have asked for any more from a holiday.

My soundtrack to that summer was the new Suede album "Head Music". It clearly wasn't Suede's album, in fact it was nowhere near the standard set by their debut, "Dog Man Star" or "Coming Up". It was a glittering summer album, jam-packed full of huge indie pop anthems. It was a bright light in what was a grim year for new music. With the Slade-esque stomp of "Can't Get Enough" and the sway along majesty of "Everything Will Flow", it was an album that I would listen to at least once a day. I was determined to follow on from moving into our house and Bulgaria by enjoying the rest of the summer, and "Head Music" was the glorious musical accompaniment. The only other new albums that got airtime in my room were; The Chemical Brothers "Surrender", Shack "HMS Fable" and Mogwai's sublime "Come On Die Young".

That Morris Man You Like

DESPITE my previous run-in with the Big Boss, I had managed to keep hold of my job and was even beginning to flourish. It was a role that could mess with your brain if you let it, talking to people about their mortgage arrears and potential repossessions all day. We would regularly hear agonising tales of genuine tragedy from customers, as well as receiving threats of violence and the "I know where you live, you wanker" responses to our phone calls. Amongst the 10 of us on the Collections section we forged a team spirit which would invariably see us lightening our collective mood in the pub after work on a Friday. It was on one of these pub trips that I ended up chatting to Vicky, who was our Team Leader and thus my boss. She was friendly, seemed reasonably well adjusted and was easy to talk banal rubbish to. By the 3rd drink she was telling me how her ex-boyfriend had left her, that she didn't think she would ever find anyone ever again and that she now lived on her own. She was on the 'talking rubbish' side of tipsy so I didn't think anything of her shouting into my ear, over the noise of one of our lot murdering "Sit Down" on the karaoke:

'You're such a good listener, how are you single? If I were 5 years younger....'

Our Friday night work trips to the pub were often supplemented by members of our team bumping into each other on Saturday night trips to the meat markets of the city centre. It was on such a night, in 5th Avenue, that I bumped into Vicky and we shared a round of Tequila Slammers at the bar. She paid for them, she was my boss after all. Buoyed by the alcoholic slap round the face, we stumbled onto the packed dancefloor. After the fog cleared in my head, I indicated by the use of universally recognised nightclub sign language that, "I don't dance" and that I was going back to the bar. I didn't expect her to follow me, but she did by putting her hand inside mine to negotiate the writhing mass of bodies that were between us and another drink. It was only as she held my hand that I even got an inkling that something might happen between us. She was my boss and she was a fully fledged woman being 28 to my 23. Vicky was petite and (just about) 5 foot tall, with a cute face and dirty blonde bob. In many ways she looked like Amy, but six inches shorter. We carried on talking, ordering ridiculously priced shots and ignoring the gyrating bodies around us and in a darkened corner of the club, at the traditional kissing time of 1.50am, the inevitable happened.

Despite the age gap and the fact that she was my boss, we agreed to meet up later that week for a drink, whilst also pledging to "behave normally" at work. From that first drunken exchange, we knew that we weren't going to last forever but we liked each other, were both single and had fun in each other's company so decided to give it a go. However, our being together did cause Vicky a lot of stress as it broke a strict rule our employers had about bosses fraternising with members of their team. Nobody at work, other than Vicky's closest friends, were allowed to know about our relationship. She would be a bag of nerves in the office, terrified that the Big Boss would find out about us. I probably didn't help the situation by purposefully winding her up, leaving notes on her desk saying things like "looking forward to going out later", or trying to grab a kiss from her in the car park as we all left for the evening.

By the third week of us seeing each other, Vicky's nerves were shredded and the paranoia about "work finding out" dominated every second we spent together. Even on nights out, we would have to get separate taxis back to her house just in case someone saw us getting into a cab together. I would then have to get the driver to stop half a mile from her place and walk the rest of the way, keeping an eye out in case I spotted anyone from work. This was our weekly routine despite Vicky living at least 5 miles away from anyone else that we worked with. We would sit in her front room, watching a film or listening to some music and she would draw all the curtains, just in case someone from work knocked on the front door unexpectedly.

The paranoia wasn't the strangest thing about Vicky though. That accolade went to her complete and utter obsession with Friends. In 1999, most of the country appeared to be in love with the japes and scrapes that the coffee loving thirty somethings from New York found themselves involved in. I watched the show, like everybody else. Vicky was different though, she was obsessed with it. Now that's not a word that I throw around lightly, but I knew obsession when I saw it and Vicky was hooked. She would insert dialogue from the show into everyday conversations and I'm pretty sure she thought that the character of Phoebe was based on her personality. We could be having a perfectly normal conversation about where to meet for a drink or what to watch on the TV when, rather than say a simple "No", or "No thanks", she would put on her Phoebe accent and loudly exclaim, 'Ohhhhh No!'. I would paint on a tight, cold smile and look to change the subject. I got increasingly worried one night, when she spent ten minutes trying unsuccessfully to get me to put on a Joey accent and ask her, 'How you doin'?' as we made our way up the stairs.

We had some mildly enjoyable nights out during our 6 weeks together but we didn't match. We didn't want the same things in the short or long-term. We were never going to last forever, we both knew that. Even when using the in-jokes that every couple needs to distinguish themselves from the masses, we would manage to annoy each other. She knew I wasn't keen on the Friends chatter and I could take her from smiling to livid in less than a minute by starting to sing 'Desiree' by Neil Diamond. I would tell her that it was just a song that I loved to sing but she'd bare her teeth upon hearing the opening lines, about a boy becoming a man in the hands of an older woman.

'There's only 5 year's difference between us for god's sake. Who the hell listens to Neil Diamond anyway? You're 23 not 63.'

I would just carry on warbling, occasionally forcing the name Vicky into Desiree's place in the song, which would usually see her storm off in a huff.

One Tuesday night in July she asked me to hers for dinner. Nothing unusual about that, other than she had informed me to, "Not bring any clothes for work tomorrow and don't bother bringing any beer.' I didn't need to be Sherlock to work out that we were heading for the "it's not you, it's me" talk.

We didn't get round to eating dinner. In fact, I'm not even sure she'd made any. I was hardly through the front door before she kicked off the "it's not you, it's me" talk. As she began her obviously well rehearsed speech, I stood there thinking, 'Wow, this is a novelty, someone other than me being at fault for a relationship ending'. To cut a long drawn out explanation short, especially as it was littered with quotes from Friends, Vicky had realised that she needed to get back together with her ex-boyfriend, Adrian. He had called her the week before when I was at her local pub watching the football and told her through a flood of tears how much he still loved her and wanted her back. She realised in that phone call that he was the love of her life and they had spent the last few days planning how their new life together would pan out.

I didn't have anything to say. I wasn't upset, it was going to end sometime soon and I certainly wasn't going to miss the Phoebe impressions. I gave her a quick hug and a, 'Good luck with it all, I'll see you at work in the morning.' I thought it really was that simple, no problem, no big deal. I had got to know her, enjoyed her company and my best wishes for the future were genuine. She looked a bit gutted that I hadn't burst into tears or made a scene that she could recall to her mates but I was already on my way to her front door, heading home.

Work was difficult for the next couple of weeks. I was fine, but Vicky had got it into her head that I was upset about us splitting up, and would be constantly checking that I was ok. I exploited her concern a couple of times by telling her that 'Yeah, I think I am too upset to work this afternoon", so that she would let me leave early and I could join my mates in the pub.

I had spent the previous couple of months looking at jobs that would enable me to leave the building society. After many failed applications, in August I was offered a 4 month contract working for a college in Cambridge on their student admissions desk. Despite my dad going absolutely bonkers at me leaving a permanent job for a temporary contract, I knew it was a chance I should take. It wasn't the opportunity of a lifetime, or anything like that, but it was a chance to do something different.

After accepting the job offer, I went into work the next morning to hand in my notice. This meant that I had to give my resignation letter to Vicky. When I got into the office, she was in a meeting so I left the letter on her chair and got on with my day. I told my other workmates, who were all happy for me. It wasn't until dinnertime that Vicky came back to our office and read my letter. As she read the two lines of text, her hand went to her mouth in an exaggerated show of despair and she ran melodramatically from the office. One of the girls went to make sure she was ok and came back with a tear-stained note which read "Meet me in the canteen please, Vicky. x"

Never one to miss a trip to the canteen when I should have been working, off I went. I got a cup of tea and wandered over to a table in the far corner where I found this woman that, 6 weeks ago I had thought of as cute, hunched over a table in floods of tears, with mascara and hair everywhere. She looked like Marilyn Manson after he had finished a particularly sweaty gig. With an anguished howl, she opened up with; 'You're leaving because of me, because I split up with you, I know you are. I've ruined your life, it's all my fault.'

Blimey, wasn't expecting her to say that.

Me – 'Errr....honestly Vic' it's not because of you. You knew I'd been applying for other jobs.'

Vicky – 'Noooooooooooooooooooooooo, you're lying. I know you're leaving because I broke your heart.'

Try as I might, I couldn't stop the giggle rising up from deep inside me, forcing tea to explode out of my mouth, up my nose and all over the the table.

Vicky – 'Are you laughing?'

Me, spluttering and thinking "Jeez, she fancies herself"- 'No, of course not, my tea just went down the wrong way. Sorry about that. Anyway, look, I promise it's not about you. We had fun, it ended, we've both moved on. Me leaving is just about my new job, I promise.'

Vicky – 'It's like on that tape that you made me by that Morris man you like, about heartbreak and.....'

Me – 'It's Morrissey.'

Vicky – 'What is?'

Me – 'The name of the singer, it's not Morris, it's Morrissey.'

Vicky – It's like the song when he sings about sitting in the bar with his head on the bar. That will be you now, sitting with your head on the bar thinking about having to leave your job because of what I've done.'

After a quick ponder, I realised she meant the lyric in "The More You Ignore Me, The Closer I Get". That was the first track on the tape that I'd made her. I was just about to ask her if that was the only song she had listened to when the howling started up again.

Vicky – 'You have to understand, I had to go back to Adrian. He's the Ross to my Rachel. Your Morris man would understand that, wouldn't he?'

Me – 'It's MORRISSEY! Not a difficult name to remember is it? Anyway, it doesn't matter whether he would understand or not, I am finishing here next Friday and it is nothing at all to do with you going back to your ex-boyfriend, ok? Sod this, can you tell everyone I've gone home sick, I'm off to the pub.'

Vicky – calling after me 'You won't find the answers to your troubles at the bottom of a glass, Jay. You know where I am if you want to talk……'

She may have carried on talking but I was already out of the canteen and heading to my car. I left the next week, with Vicky taking a day's annual leave on my final day so that, to quote from a note she sent me, "we don't both get upset about you leaving because of me."

The following Monday I packed the glove box full of specially created compilation tapes with titles such as 'Early Morning Indie Tunes' and 'Friday Night Drive Home' and began my drive to Cambridge with a smile on my face. I came home with the same smile thanks to a day spent talking to students and not worrying about profits, arrears or the number of calls I'd made. The upside to the commute was that I got to spend 2 hours a day driving on the motorway with Morrissey or Billy Bragg pounding out of the stereo whilst I screeched along.

I met up with Amy a couple of times during my spell at the college. We went for coffee or lunch, never a beer anymore and it was fine. It wasn't difficult or full of stilted conversation, it was just fine. We had moved firmly into friends territory, talking about our plans for the future and her telling me that

I "needed to get a proper girlfriend and settle down". That was a conversation that I found odd to be having with my (ex-) girlfriend of 3 years, but never mind. I would tell her that I had no intention of settling down anytime soon as I was enjoying life too much. We both knew that was a slight exaggeration and I suspect we both knew that I would sit there and daydream about her saying, "Shall we just get back together?" Instead we maintained a characteristically English silence on the matter.

We were getting on so well as friends that I even treated Amy and my mum to tickets to see Billy Bragg and the wonderful Kate Rusby at Cambridge Corn Exchange. The 3 of us sat in the upper circle of the venue, stone cold sober, with my mum being extra careful not to mention anything about mine and Amy's relationship. I knew that she wanted to break down in tears, grab Amy's arm and beg her to take me back, but she managed to hold it together. It didn't occur to me to ask Amy what her new boyfriend thought about her going to a gig with her ex and his mum.

That gig was a dry run to see if we could have an enjoyable, civilised night out together now that we were just friends. The reason that we needed a dry run was that I had 2 tickets for the Homelands dance festival. I'd bought the tickets the previous year, as soon as they went on sale, to try and convince Amy I could change and go to gigs that she liked. In fairness, she had tried to persuade me not to buy them, but I had been convinced that by the time the festival rolled around we would be back together. The decent thing for me to have done would have been to give her the tickets and tell her to go and have a good time with her new man. On the other hand, I'd shelled out £60, had never been to a dance music festival before and the Chemical Brothers were headlining. Not for the first time where Amy was concerned, I decided not to do the decent thing. I don't know whether it was her desire to see the Chemical Brothers or her feeling that, as I had bought the ticket for her, she should come with me, but she did.

The long train journey to Winchester should probably have been quite awkward, as we were now a couple that had grown up together but had been apart for almost a year, but it wasn't. We chatted about anything and everything other than our respective love lives, both determined to make the most of the day out. Homelands was billed as taking place from 1pm-5am but, having never been to such an event before, we weren't really sure when it would all start to get going. We had both been to plenty of indie festivals though, so we knew the score. When we got to the site at 2pm I rushed straight to the solitary beer tent, which was unusually deserted, to get us both a drink.

While watching the early afternoon DJ's and live acts, which included a cracking set from Asian Dub Foundation, we kept drinking. In the style of any indie festival we'd ever been to, by that time we were both merrily half-cut. The only problem was, by 8pm at Glastonbury or Reading only a couple more acts were due to play, at Homelands it hadn't even really started. By 11pm, I was hammered, dancing around to the DJ brilliance of Paul Oakenfold whilst Amy, who had stopped drinking, was developing a hangover. Things picked up as we got to 1am and Fatboy Slim and then The Chemical Brothers came on and got the crowd jumping. By 4am we were knackered. With the trains from Winchester not starting again until later that morning, we gratefully pounced on a couple of stray cardboard boxes, opened them out and got some kip in the middle of the festival site. We woke a couple of hours later and walked the two miles back to the station to begin the long journey home. It hadn't been a dream day out but it hadn't been a disaster, plus we got to see the Chemical Brothers. It was to be the last day out that Amy and I would have.

Life was bumbling along quite obligingly with work, a new house and going to plenty of gigs and football matches with my mates. I was determined to regenerate, Dr Who style, into a simple soul and it felt like that was all I needed. I also entered my last extended love affair of the millennium when I stumbled across the Tindersticks. Their 'Simple Pleasure' album was released in September and it was the comfy set of slippers to accompany the pyjama top and bottoms that Moz and Billy Bragg provided me with. Stuart Staples voice was like a hot cup of tea with not quite enough milk, a tasty concoction with a hint of a tang and hidden layers of taste. I put the 6 minutes of defining glory that was the albums final track 'CF GF' on to a tape and would listen to it over and over again. Nothing else on the tape, just that song recorded 15 times. I explored their rich back catalogue and found albums that convinced me to buy cheap old man's suits from charity shops for £3 a go in an attempt to be part of the Tindersticks gang. Songs like 'Jism', 'Travelling Light' and the duet with Isabella Rossellini, 'A Marriage Made In Heaven', were the soundtrack to my autumn, lighting the candle in my brain and running the bath at the same time.

Elvis Boxers & Matching Socks

WHILST comfortably wrapped up in a Tindersticks world, I wandered into my final relationship of the millennium. Sam was the best friend of Jacko's girlfriend, Claire. I had talked to her on group nights out in Peterborough over the previous couple of years and despite being a bit full of herself, she was an infectious character. She was a ball of energy whenever she was out, determined to get the party started. Her personality was a heady mix of cultures with Sri Lankan parentage and a wannabe cockney attitude due to her living in the commuter town of Hitchin. Until that summer I'd never considered that anything would ever happen between us. She had, up until recently, been with the same boyfriend for years and there had never been any kind of spark between us. By the time I was looking to sneak out of clubs and home to my Morrissey CD's & a cup of tea she would be in the middle of the dancefloor flinging her arms around to the latest chart tunes.

Then, during one particularly drunken night out, the kind of evening that's all Sambuca and revelations that you regret making public the next morning, Claire casually said to me, "Sam really fancies you". That was the first time that had happened to me since school and I had thought that, by 23, we'd grown out of the "my mate fancies you" approach. I leant against the bar of The Solstice and watched Sam chatting to my mates, arms whirling around trying desperately to squeeze as many words as possible into every sentence. I knew that we were very different people but what harm could it do to act on Claire's covert information?

I had resigned myself to a contented single life with my mates, Morrissey and The Posh taking centre stage. I wasn't sad about the thought of not getting into another relationship, in some ways such a life sounded like heaven. However, stood at the bar that night, swaying from the Sambuca rattling my brain, I thought that I should take a chance. A woman fancied me, she was single and so was I. Why was I even thinking? I knew that I should have been over there buying her a drink.

My self doubt soon wrestled back its controlling interest in my brain and despite Claire reassuring me, I wasn't convinced that Sam fancied me. I wasn't being self deprecating but why would she? I was a Moz fanatic with a £6 haircut, which now incorporated ridiculously long Weller-esque sideburns. I was still dressing like Britpop ruled the world. Everything about me was firmly anchored in 1995 and refusing to set sail for the new millennium. I was a miserable sod as well, at least half the time. Sam was one of those people that thought me being miserable was an act that I was putting on to be deadpan and funny. It wasn't and she would learn that lesson the hard way.

It was whilst thinking "why would she fancy me?" that I remembered Sam was a big fan of Gaz Coombes from Supergrass. So that was it, my sideburns had finally worked their magic.

With Sam taking the lead in the flirting stakes we ended up in the familiar 1.50am clinch. The party eventually moved back to Deano's house, where it quickly descended into the host making everyone drink shots and him crooning along to Tracey Chapman's debut album at 5am. He was our mate, we were used to it, but to anyone that didn't know him they must have worried for his mental health. Sat on Deano's sofa, with "Fast Car" pumping out of the stereo loud enough to wake the dead,

Sam and I decided that we would put aside our recent bad experiences with long-term partners and the blindingly obvious differences in our personalities and 'just have some fun'.

Most of our friends, Claire aside, expressed their bafflement at our agreement to share emotions and bodily fluids. I knew that this wasn't going to be one of history's more memorable love affairs when Sam repeatedly told anyone that would listen: "We are nothing like each other at all. We are the odd couple, we don't even really get on that well, but sod it, who cares?" I doubt that Elizabeth Taylor introduced people to Richard Burton in such a manner.

Sam worked for a film production company and was full of ambition, vigour and desire for life. I was me.

She worked in London and was in love with the metropolis. She would insist on us going to trendy bars, where the doorman would look at my Smiths "Rank" t-shirt and openly grimace. Sam would know most of the clientele in such establishments through work and for the first few weeks of our relationship she would introduce me to such people, stand back and expect conversation to flow. It didn't.

On a dank October afternoon, it dawned on Sam that I wasn't "the one". We had met a group of her media friends in Soho and gone to a fancy bar, the kind of place where you have to know a member and the secret password to get in. Sam was ridiculously overexcited to be gaining entry to such a place and was giddy at the thought that "Chris Evans might be inside". Inside, it seemed to my non-media trained eyes to be just like any other poncey bar in central London, with overpriced drinks, high backed chairs and the unmistakable air of snobbery.

All was going reasonably well for the first couple of hours as I sipped at my whiskey and water (they didn't serve pints). I smiled when I thought the conversation needed it, and nodded when all eyes occasionally turned my way.

The problem came when, at 4.45pm, I made what I thought was a reasonable request to the barman:

Me: 'Excuse me, is there a TV anywhere that I can watch the football results on?'

Barman – A 3 second delay while he takes in the preposterous question that I have just dared to ask, before politely sneering, 'I'm sure there is a television somewhere showing such things sir, but not in this bar. We don't show any sports here.'

Right on cue, the doorman blocks out the light over my right shoulder.

Doorman - 'Is there a problem, Piers?'

Barman - 'This gentleman wants to watch the football results.'

Doorman – turns to me, with his face contorting into a menacing grin: 'Do we have a problem, sir?'

Me: 'Not unless asking a civil question is a problem?'

Doorman – 'It would appear our establishment isn't suited to your tastes. I think it may be time for you to leave sir.'

Me: now laughing, loudly; 'That suits me just fine my old mate, give me 30 seconds to tell my girlfriend, then I'm out of here.'

I turned to see that everyone in the bar had stopped their conversation and was looking at me. Sam was stood with her mouth wide open and my first thought was that she looked like a sleeping Homer Simpson. As she regained her composure, and her voice, she looked more like a fuming Montgomery Burns.

Sam: 'Why did you have to show me up by asking for the football?'

Me: 'How the hell is me asking to watch the results such an issue to you or the soddin' barman?'

Sam: 'I'm in the middle of a discussion about a new TV project and I don't want to go yet. It's the big league in here Jay, can't you just enjoy it?'

Me: 'It's not really me is it, this place?'

Sam: 'You are such an inverted snob, you know that, right? If a place doesn't sell lager, crisps, and show the match on a big screen then it must be snobby and not for you.'

Me: 'You can call me what you like, but right now I need to find out how The Posh got on this afternoon away at York City. Look, I'll find a proper pub, watch the results then give you a call in an hour.....'

With a final shake of her achingly trendy, slightly too short hair, she turned back to her conversation and the hulking doorman was once again invading my shadow.

I left without saying another word to either of them, convinced that I was the one in the right. I went for a couple of pints in the pubs down Berwick Street to calm down, then gave her a call from my first mobile phone, to see if she fancied coming to meet me. The call was very brief. I'm not sure if that was because she knew I was conscious that this new-fangled mobile technology was costing me 50p a minute, or if she just wanted to get rid of me and back to her media chums. Either way, she made it crystal clear that she was staying in the bar and enjoying herself, which suited me. It left me free to wander the record shops of Soho and stop off in a couple of pubs for a pint and a read of the paper.

The Posh got a hard-earned 0-0 draw at York as well, so the day had definitely taken a turn in the right direction.

In fairness to Sam, as well as the god-awful bars her media friends liked to frequent, she did also introduce me to the brilliant "Bradleys Spanish Bar". I fell for this tiny drinking establishment, situated just off Oxford Street, as soon as I walked in, saw that they had an old vinyl jukebox and that "This Charming Man" was on it. I must have spent at least £50 playing songs on that jukebox that autumn while drinking pints of San Miguel and listening to Sam talk. That's how our days out tended to work, I would listen to her talk and she would indulge me by coming with me to record shops and sitting in pubs that had a jukebox.

As well as our trips to London, Sam and her mates would often come to Peterborough and, along with my mates, we would all go out as a group. Sam and I never did anything like go for a meal or a relaxing walk. Sam didn't do quiet. So that we could spend time together, despite us living 50 miles apart, I would regularly finish work in Cambridge and drive over to her house for the night. On her dad's orders, I would sleep in the downstairs bedroom and Sam stayed in hers. Prior to that, we would spend much of our time sitting in her room listening to Supergrass or Morrissey and talking. I didn't mind a chat but never considered myself one of life's leading conversationalists. Sam loved to talk. She talked more than anyone I'd ever met. Whereas I saw silence as something to enjoy and relax into, Sam saw it as a challenge. She would have to find something to prattle on about to fill any available space. At times her need to talk to me or, as often happened, at me, was quite endearing. In other situations, such as the one and only time that we went to the cinema, it made me want to ram the extra large tub of popcorn into her mouth to fill the chattering gap. Outside the cinema, as we waited for the bus, I stood and sang 'Rabbit' by Chas 'N' Dave over and over in an attempt to drown her out. I don't think she even noticed.

Sam was the first person I'd ever gone to gigs with that just wouldn't shut up while the bands were playing. Going to gigs with Doody, Jacko, Amy or anyone else, meant that an unwritten rule came into play, namely that you could talk before the band came on and between songs but never during a song.

If you needed to let your mates know that you were off

to the bar during a song, you would nudge them to get their attention and use the universally recognised signal for "fancy a pint?", by raising your hand to your mouth and shaking it. They would indicate their preference with a nod or shake of the head and that was that. No talking was necessary. It was a rule that everyone followed. Everyone except Sam.

It came to a head when we went to see Travis at the Shepherds Bush Empire in October. It was a gig that I didn't even want to go to but she had insisted on us getting tickets as Travis were "bad-ass". The band came onstage and started with their best tune, "All I Wanna Do Is Rock", so I settled down with my pint and a determination to enjoy the gig. Sam on the other hand just couldn't shut up. I'd politely asked her twice not to talk during the first couple of tunes and as the band kicked into "Driftwood", five songs in, I was joining in with the couple behind us who were issuing growled "Shhhhhhh's" in Sam's direction. By the time Travis were singing "Why Does It Always Rain on Me?", Sam and I were outside in the pouring rain having a blazing row. She couldn't understand my "pathetic indie geek attitude to just having a chat during a song". I had lost the will to live. As we got soaked to the skin, screaming in the street at each other, the band struck up their final song, "Happy" and I vowed to never to go to another gig with her. Our relationship was already starting to hit the rocks, with us being such different people and enjoying very different social occasions. Whilst she was off to a party at some z-list TV celebrities house, I was back at the Empire watching Gomez with my mate, Jake. She rang me late that night, spangled, from the party, telling me what an amazing time she was having and that I was missing out. I was more than happy, standing and jigging my leg along to the storming "Whippin' Piccadilly".

Some successful relationships are built upon the fact that the two people in it are polar opposites. Such couples work out how their differences can fit together to ensure they have a happy life together. It's all about give and take. With mine and

297

Sam's relationship we didn't care enough, we both just wanted to take and force the other to compromise. In many ways it was a relationship we both needed as it was our first serious one after splitting up with our long term partners. Sam had spent her university years with a bloke called Steve who, after a couple of years of her constant talking, had lost interest in their relationship and spent upwards of 8 hours a day playing Championship Manager. Eventually, he had decided that he needed to pull himself together and ditched virtual football management and Sam, just after they had both graduated. She was hurt by it all and still struggling to understand why he had left her. One night, when the Bacardi and Coke had calmed her need to talk constant piffle, she told me that Gene's "Olympian" had been her and Steve's special song. It was a cracking tune but I was slightly taken aback by her putting it on the stereo, promptly bursting into tears and then expecting me to give her a hug. I wasn't a psychologist but I began to wonder if Sam was really over Steve leaving her.

Autumn also brought the news that I had been hoping for. Morrissey was going to tour the UK to end the millennium. The dates included 3 nights at the Kentish Town Forum. It had been 3 years since I had seen him play live thanks to a lack of UK gigs to support "Maladjusted". With The Forum only having a 2000 capacity, we knew that getting tickets would be tough but on the morning they went on sale, Jake and I had both taken the day off work and were camped on the phone lines from 8.55am. By 9.30am, after constantly hitting the redial button, we got through and secured ourselves two tickets.

On 14th November 1999, we headed to London for what would be my last gig of the millennium. Morrissey was on sparkling form that night, with hundreds of disciples doing all they could to invade the stage and throw their arms around the messiah.

With sweat dripping from the walls, he rattled through gems like, "Hairdresser on Fire", "Sunny" and "November Spawned a

Monster" as the floor of the venue shook with people jumping up and down in unbridled joy. The highlights were a riotous rendition of "Speedway" where every man and woman in the crowd seemed to be screaming the lyrics back at him whilst grasping at their Morrissey t-shirt, and the magnificent call to vegetarianism of "Meat Is Murder". I was fed up of being vegetarian, sick of the difficulties life threw at me when not eating meat. I was bored of the mickey taking from my mates and having to explain in restaurants, parties and, most frustratingly of all, on holidays that I didn't eat meat. For the first time since turning vegetarian, I was giving serious consideration to eating meat again. The sound of "Meat Is Murder" was all I needed to convince me to carry on.

Despite being without a record contract or any interest from the music press, the tour sold out almost instantly and, on that final London date, Morrissey knew that, as he looked out across the crowd, he was still our "Masters Voice". It was an emotional gig for Moz and the crowd, as it had been so long since we had got to hear those songs and to show our adoration. Jake and I stood at the end embraced in a huge man-hug, knowing that we had just witnessed something very special. Jake wasn't usually one for emotions but that night saw us leave the venue high on life. It had been a magical night, a night that would've been the perfect end to the millennium.

As we headed into December, the world was beginning to worry about the potential Armageddon that would be wreaked by the Millennium Bug. It was utter nonsense of course, and our computers just ticked over with the usual mechanical click rather than the thud of imminent worldwide disaster.

The other event that had everyone running around in a frenzy was Millennium Eve. For Sam, it had to be the "biggest night out ever". I couldn't think of anything worse. I wasn't a fan of New Year's Eve in a normal year and this was the New Year's Eve to end all New Year's Eves.

Sam and her mates had decided that the best way to welcome in the dawn of a new age was to stand in the freezing cold at the side of the Thames and watch some fireworks. Jacko and I hatched a plan to get into a pub in central London and stay there, but we knew that idea would be scuppered by the boundless enthusiasm of Sam and Claire. I made it bluntly apparent that I didn't think Sam's plan was a good one but she was a one woman millennium whirlwind who didn't have time to bother with what I thought about the festivities.

A week before Christmas, I overheard her talking to her sister about the big night out:

'I know Jay would rather spend the evening sat at home with the curtains drawn, listening to music, eating takeaway pizza and drinking beer but tough, he can bloody well come to London and enjoy himself.'

Fair play to Sam, she knew me better than I thought she did. She had described my dream NYE even if she wasn't going to actually allow me to live it.

The holiday period flew past in the traditional blur of presents, drinks and late night parties at Deano's house. Before we knew it, the day was upon us. The plan was to meet at Hitchin station and get the train to London. Before we had even left, I had delayed us by insisting upon finding a member of staff who could give me solid confirmation on how we would get back from Kings Cross later that night. Sam and her gang had been happy to conclude "we will get back somehow". I needed a firm plan in place and, fortunately, the station manager was on hand to assure me that trains would be running late into the night.

The one concession that Jacko and I had won was that we would make an early start and get to London for 5pm. Our theory being that we could get everyone safely ensconced in a cordial old mans pub, in this case The Lamb & Flag near Covent Garden, and hope that after a few drinks everyone would want to stay in the warm rather than traipse to the river for the fireworks. Sam saw right through our plan and, as I handed her a 3rd drink of the night, growled at me through a smile, "You won't win, I will get everyone to the river for midnight". Which, as I had bought her a double gin and tonic, I thought was a little ungrateful, if very perceptive.

After a few drinks had warmed everyone up, I tried a new tactic. With Sam's planned 9.30pm pub departure time looming, I tried my best to be morose when speaking to her, in the hope that she would just explode and scream at me to "just sod off home, you miserable git". She was wise to such a tactic and again hissed at me through her painted on smile; 'You won't ruin this for me, you will be coming to the river, Jay. You will have fun.'

She was getting right on my nerves now. I was being a childish prat but that was a key element of my personality. Her boundless enthusiasm wasn't infectious, it was bloody annoying. I spent the next hour grumbling into my pint while unsuccessfuy trying to persuade the landlord to put "The Queen Is Dead" on the pub stereo.

Before Tesco clawed its way into Covent Garden with its "flagship" store, nowhere in that area sold alcohol to take away. So, after leaving the warmth of the Lamb & Flag at the appointed hour, as per my girlfriends instructions, we spent the next half an hour wandering around trying to locate an off licence. Eventually, Jacko and I decided to walk back into Soho to a "Bargain Booze" emporium to pick up enough alcohol for everyone. I tried again to get him to join me in a coup to scupper the river and fireworks plan, but he had long ago accepted his fate and wanted to; 'Just get on with it and try and enjoy the night. C'mon it might be a good laugh.'

Loaded down with cans of Carling Premier and bottles of blue WKD, we made it back to our intrepid band of freezing adventurers and began the walk to the riverside. It was a bitterly cold night with a touch of sleet in the air and I dragged my feet at the back of the group, swigging from a can and eating my Smiths Square Crisps with the facial expression of a man consuming his last meal before being taken to the gallows at nearby Tower Hill. Up at the front of, Sam was holding her left arm up in the air and barking instructions, looking like one of those tour guides that escort Japanese tourists through airports.

It came as no surprise to anyone, other than the eternally optimistic Sam, that we couldn't get anywhere near the river due to the sheer number of people that had decided to waste their last moments of the millennium in the same bleak fashion as us. As with any big occasion in London, people had been camping out for days to get what they considered to be the perfect spot. Our group squeezed into a spot opposite the Oxo Tower which was at least 100 yards from the river, in a small wooded area next to a block of flats. It wasn't exactly the view that any of us had envisaged but everyone got stuck into the alcohol to keep warm and raise their spirits. I cradled my can and realised that even if I'd wanted to, I couldn't now get out of the foul mood that I'd created for myself. I had gone too far this time.

I did my best to smile and stay out of the way but by 11pm, my cheerleaderesque girlfriend had wound me up just one notch too many with her constant talk of "having an amazing time":

Me: 'The only way this is amazing, is that its amazingly bloody awful. It's cold, boring and we are miles from the river. We should have stayed in the pub.'

Sam: 'Only you could moan about tonight Jay. You do realise THIS IS THE MILLENIUM EVE!

Me: 'Thanks for shouting, I wasn't aware of it until then. You're right, now I know what eve it is for sure, I can go back to my patch of frozen woodland and enjoy myself.'

Sam (now bouncing up and down and sporting an inane grin, like a kid on a pogo-stick who has just swallowed his elder brothers secret stash of E's thinking they were smarties): 'Come on misery guts, just let loose and enjoy yourself. Who knows what tomorrow will bring? Just enjoy tonight.'

The sheer unrelenting positivity flowing out of her had caused a nervous tic to develop in my right eyelid.

Sam: 'This is history right here. You love prattling on about history, well here we are, right in the middle of a historic event.'

Me: 'Are we bollocks! We're standing in the cold waiting for £100,000 of taxpayers money to be wasted on 10 minutes of fireworks. That's all we are doing.'

Sam (still disconcertingly bouncing up and down): 'You know what, Jay? When we first met, I thought your miserable git act was hysterical. I was convinced it was a performance and even when I realised it wasn't, that it really was your personality, I thought, 'He will end up having fun nights out with me and will drop the moody stuff". You know what though? You are a miserable, self-centred, pathetic twat and I don't know why I even bother trying to make you happy.'

Me, now cracking up with laughter after her outburst; 'That's superb, Sam; you can't beat a good character assassination to end the millennium.'

Sam: 'I'm sure Morrissey would approve of you ending the millennium in a bad mood while everyone else is having the time of their lives.'

Me: 'Don't bring Moz into it.'

Sam: 'Why not? You bring him in to every other bloody aspect of our lives.'

Me: 'Oh just piss off and enjoy yourself.'

Not my wittiest ever conclusion to an argument but the

ending of her bouncing, and the hangdog look on her face was an indication that I was in danger of ruining her big night. Despite my complaining, that was the last thing I wanted to do. Well actually the last thing I wanted to do was to be stood under a tree, 100 yards from the Thames in the cold, but ruining Sam's night was the second to last thing I wanted to do.

I looked at my watch, seeing it was 10.45pm, and made the mental calculation as to whether I could get to Kings Cross and back to Peterborough before midnight. It was impossible and I silently cursed myself for not bringing that inevitable argument to a head an hour earlier.

Sam and I didn't speak again until five to midnight, when I decided that I had better apologise and not start the 2000's in the middle of a row with my girlfriend. I offered up a paper thin apology and tried to smile sweetly. She gave me a low level scowl to indicate 'this isn't over', before kicking back into cheerleader mode and urging our group to remember this "never to be forgotten moment". I mistakenly thought she meant me apologising but, as the chimes of Big Ben blasted out from the speakers spread along the embankment, I realised that I was, possibly, being a little self-centred.

I would have left it there. I had made my apology and wanted to get on with the night. Unfortunately, a now clearly inebriated, Sam couldn't resist biting back:

'Don't pretend that you're enjoying yourself Jay, we all know you've spent the night wishing you were back in Peterborough with your mates.'

Me: 'What? I just apologised even though I had nothing to apologise for in the hope that we could have a decent end to the night. Just get off my case will you and get on with enjoying the, "Never to be forgotten moment".'

Sam: 'See this is what I mean, you're impossible. I was just saying to the girls…

10

...I can't do this anymore....

9

.....I can't put up with your....

8

...Morrissey obsessed miserable bastardness...

7

Me: Are you going to....

6

....finish with me here.....

5

...That would be mental, even for you....

4

.....what a night this is....

3

Sam: Oh just piss off....

2

....Just go away........

1

...you miserable c.....

HAPPY NEW YEAR

The dawn of the new millennium had saved me from being called a c***.

Conversation over, I walked over to give my old mate Jacko the obligatory new year hug, just as Sam was leading the rest of our group and some bemused American tourists in a dog-eared version of "Auld Lang Syne."

In fairness, the firework display across The Thames that night was pretty spectacular. As with every firework display

I've ever been too though, 30 seconds after they had finished, everyone was stood around wondering what to do next.

After much shrugging of shoulders and group discussions around "what shall we do now?", we decided to head back to Covent Garden tube station and see if any pubs were still open along the way. I walked ahead, still outwardly projecting my first bad mood of the new millennium, whilst giggling inside about almost being called, what we in Peterborough call, a 'Cambridge United Northampton Town', as the clock struck 12.

As we trudged towards Covent Garden, the darkened streets resembled the scene from a post apocalyptic film, with debris from the night everywhere but with very few functioning human beings around. All the pubs en route were closed and the people we did meet, who no doubt half an hour previously were delighted to be in London celebrating the new millennium, were now furious that no pubs or, more importantly, tube stations, were open. We were left with no option but to wearily trudge the mile and a half to Kings Cross.

I strode on alone, well in advance of the group, Discman and headphones on. My bad mood dissipated as I was walking along the deserted streets of London with Morrissey singing "Now My Heart Is Full" in my ears. They say whatever you do on 1st January, you will do for the rest of the year, well walking alone whilst listening to Moz for a whole year would have been a dream come true.

It dawned on me during that walk that the only part of my life that was getting me down was my relationship with Sam. As the rain began to fall, my alcohol addled mind began to wonder what had become of the girls I had gone out with in the last decade. In such moments I convinced myself that they were all off having a joyful and exciting life. Amy would be in Australia with her fella, having followed her sister out there, suntanned and putting another shrimp on the barbie. She wouldn't be thinking of me or every so often drawing the curtains, putting on

Suede's 'Coming Up' and drinking a bottle of port. Jo would have gone to live on a hippy commune, listening to Ozric Tentacles every day and surrounded by peace and love. Kate, Jess and Vicky would all no doubt have gone on to find happiness and told their partners about this speccy, Morrissey obsessed prat that they once had the misfortune to go out with.

I had to give up daydreaming at that point, as I'd reached Kings Cross only to find that the last train to Hitchin was leaving in 5 minutes. As I had walked on ahead of the group, I had to scream at them in my foghorn voice to 'Hurry up, the train's going NOW'. As I stood watching them all pound the streets like Linford Christie, I focused on Sam and decided that I wanted to give our relationship once last try. I wasn't sure it could work or even if I really wanted it to but I figured it was worth giving it a go.

We piled onto the packed train as the doors were closing and due to being squashed into whatever space we could find, I didn't get to tell Sam my grand plan on that leg of the journey. Upon reaching Hitchin, amid a flurry of hugs, we all said our goodbyes and Sam and I began the mile or so walk back to her house.

This was my big opportunity.

Me: 'Sam, I just wanted to say.....'

Sam: 'Whatever it is Jay, I don't want to hear it. I've had enough of you tonight. You just can't help spoiling things can you? I honestly think you might be mentally ill. You're so certain that bloody Morrissey holds all life's answers that you can't think for yourself anymore. You know he probably doesn't mean most of his lyrics don't you? I bet he sits there writing them, chuckling to himself and thinking: 'This is a load of meaningless rubbish but my div fans will lap it up like it's an extract from the bible.' He is just putting lyrics in to fit a tune but all over the world there are thousands of idiots just like you who treat his every muttering like its an inspired message from God. Why don't you go and find one of those female idiots? Go and live miserably ever after.'

Sensing it was not a good time to tell her that I wanted to see if we could patch up our relationship, I opted to walk on in silence. When we got back to her parents' house, she opened the door without saying a word, pecked me on the cheek, said "Goodnight" and weaved up the stairs to her bedroom. I headed to the downstairs guest room and pondered my options. With so many thoughts emerging like blisters on my brain, I couldn't settle, so decided to make a point of going upstairs to her, apologising for my moodiness, talk about our future and maybe even have a quick new millennium bonding session.

I quietly made my way up the stairs until I got to the top step and could clearly hear that Sam was on her mobile phone to someone. Being a nosey git, I decided to have a listen to her conversation rather than interrupt her. It quickly became obvious that she was talking about me and our relationship to someone I presumed to be Claire. I spent a couple of minutes listening to Sam's half of the conversation:

'It's about trying again but making it better......... I know we can do it..........I just need to talk to Jay.

I know what I want, I know how I feel.........the last few weeks have shown me exactly what I want...........I need to sit Jay down and tell him.

I can't deny how I feel any more....... I will tell Jay in the morning and everything will be fine.

At that point I was thinking, "Wow, she feels the same as me about trying again." In fact she sounded far more hopeful of our relationship being able to work than I was. To be honest, I was a bit concerned that she was going to propose to me the next morning, so enraptured did she sound with our relationship.

I tiptoed back down the stairs, safe in the knowledge that the old charm had worked it's magic on Sam. I borrowed a can of lager out of the fridge and drifted off to sleep listening to Tindersticks "Simple Pleasure", content with the world and all that it was set to offer me in the new millenia.

I slept soundly until a fully dressed Sam woke me at 8am by shaking my shoulder so violently I was worried it would dislocate.

Sam: 'Wake up, Jay. I've been awake for hours stressing about this. We need to talk, I have something to tell you.'

Me (knowing smile on my face): 'Ok sure, jump under the covers but I warn you, I've still got my lucky Elvis socks on so can't be held responsible for my actions.'

Sam: 'You're not going to make this easy are you?'

Me: (laughing) 'It's fine, come on I think we're both thinking the same thing anyway, just spit it out.'

Sam: 'I don't think we are Jay. Ok, well…. Look…. There is no easy way to say this…so I'll just say it…… I'm finishing with you. It's not you or your miserableness or Morrissey obsession, it's me, I'm going back to Steve. I still love him. I always have done and I need to go back to him. I've met him a couple of times in the last week, nothing happened though, I promise, but we talked and….well, we both miss each other and know that no other relationship comes close to ours. I'm really sorry, I don't want you to be upset but, let's be honest, we both knew that "us" wasn't going to last forever didn't we?'

Me: 'Sake, give it a rest, next you will be telling me he's the 'Ross to your Rachel.'

Sam: 'You what?'

Me: 'It doesn't matter. Wait a minute…. SHIT ME, SO THAT'S WHO YOU WERE ON THE PHONE TO LAST NIGHT!' – I dramatically threw off the duvet, to reveal the sight of my Elvis boxer shorts, which matched the socks.

Sam: now looking confused: 'What...how did you know...'

Me: 'It doesn't matter now, does it? Can you pass me my jeans please?'

She sat in silence, as I dragged on my jeans and "Viva Hate" t-shirt then pulled on my Adidas Samba Specials.

Me: 'Right, I can talk properly now I'm dressed. Well fuck me, Sam. I knew we wouldn't last forever but the first day of the new millennium? You pick your moments!'

Sam: 'I know my timing isn't great but...'

Me: 'Jeez, even on 1st January 2000, that may just be the understatement of the entire millennium. What a "never to be forgotten moment" this is turning into. When people ask me at parties in years to come; 'So Jay, what did you do for the millennium?' I can say that I stood next to a freezing cold river boring my arse off and then the next morning my girlfriend decided to pack me in and go back to her ex-boyfriend.'

Sam: Trying to inject some humour into the situation; 'Come off it Jay, you never speak to anyone at parties.'

Me: Being unnecessarily mean: 'Trust me luv, you do enough talking for the both of us at parties.'

Sam: 'Well, you won't have to put up with my incessant talking any more will you? You can spend all your time with your mates at the football or going to bloody gigs or if neither of those are available, you can do what you do best, sit in your bedroom listening to soddin' Morrissey.'

Me: Now pulling on my coat: 'Look, this is pointless, I don't have anything else to say and you've made it crystal clear where you stand. Keep my spare copy of "Strangeways Here We Come" that's in your stereo, it will give you something to remember me by. You can keep that bloody awful green shirt you bought me for Christmas, which I wore last night just to keep you happy. I'm not into the leprechaun look but, by all means see if Steve likes it, if he can squeeze into it. Right, I've said all I needed to say, have a nice life.'

I reached the bedroom door in one step, and the front door in a couple of quick strides before she hit back:

'That's it, run away, don't talk. Just run away back to your beloved Peterborough, with your mates down the pub, your crappy football club, and your Smiths CD's. Go on, sit on the train listening to Morrissey tell you how miserable you are......'

I imagine that Sam carried on talking as I opened the front door but I'd already got my headphones on and was setting out on the walk back to the station, to take the train back to my home city and my mates down the pub, while Morrissey gently sang "Everyday Is Like Sunday" just for me.

About The Author

Jamie is a 38 year old father of two whose wife has made him store his CD collection in the loft.

"I Blame Morrissey" is loosely based on his experiences of love, life and using Morrissey's lyrics to help him through his formative years. The obsession with Morrissey is, unfortunately, very real and he has the tattoos to prove it.

Jamie's wife would like to point out that, had he told her the tales contained within this book prior to their wedding, she would never have married him.

"I Blame Morrissey" is Jamie's third book and his first not based on his beloved Peterborough United FC.

Supporters List

Mum & Dad, Adrian Durham, Emma Ivison, Sinéad, Rob Tylee, Erika (Jamie's Sister), Nick Edwards, Doody, Joanne Price, Luke Harman, Neil Gillett, Pim Van Heuven, David Harwin, Stefan Krix, Sam, Davide Platania, Claire Weston, Joolz, Mr Size, Dave Fitzjohn, Anisa, Frank LeVulgar, Tom Marley, Lorna Carsley, Paul 469 Marlow, Anthony Tobin, CLEM, Hailey Shaw, Clarkypants, Carlo Restaino, John Brittain, Lisa Forbes, Sally Grimley, Simon Prior, Ads Davis, Free Kicks Foundation, Steve Fagioli, City60, Andrew Males, Neil Hubbard, Nick Warrick, Kate Downey, Terry Rowe, John Paul Delaney, Mark Oxenham, Mark Talbot, Rich Carter, Stephanie Wells, Jacko, Andrew Casey, Sean Mee, Richard Washbrooke, Sean Ingham, Ryan Hounsell, Katie Joyce, Nicola Hallas, Kalpesh Khetia, www.redorbrown. co.uk, Andy Barnett, Emma, Lee Ayres, Andrew Holt, Mike Long, Graham Harley, Andy Crane, Smithy, Graham Chard, Sharyn Savage, Donna Bishop, Faye Henchy, Christopher Sharpe, Hannah Barham, Will Fisk, Elaine O'Reilly, Paul Evers, Alison Jane Fisher, Denise Holt, Emma Jordan, Chris Walton, Kevin Rudd, Paul Butler, Mark Edwards, Alice Harriet Chapman, Lisa Marie Winter, Kellie Sullivan, Jonny Davies, Chris Slade, David Miller, Stuart 'Hank' Hancocks, Jim Saul, Dene Butler, Alan Hudson, Gemma Rollason, Annemarie Pye, Andrew Riley, Patrick Lee, Claas Spitz, Anthony Gibson, Susanne Heil, Jamie Holmes, Katie Louise Tate, John Middleton, Ivan Walker, Kassy, Kelly Stapleton, Paul Newton, Sam Clews, Kerry Richards,

Patrick Maguire, David Shepherd, Rachel Dayman, Nadine Sidhpura, Rob Burborough, Lee Morley, Michelle French, Antonietta Iacono, Samantha Hornsby, Ed Warrick, Kevin Goodacre, Craig Robinson, Andy Carter, Steve Nicholls, Neil Wright, Darren Peake, Paul Crisp, Richard Moisey, Jay Crisp, Steve Proud, Carl Howard, Ann-Marie Lawson, Stuart Maloney, Barney Rogers, Sophie Williams, Hakan (hates Morrissey), Philip Rhodes, Phil Crisp, John Donato, Simon M Stanton UTP, Chris Sweet, Robin Borgognoni, Jason Wainwright, Scott Courts, Matthew Tylee, Farah Tlemsani, Inge Kersten, Shaun Tomkiss, Paul Bamford, Karys Moffat, Ian Bradshaw, Adrian Westfield, Lyn Lockwood, Martin Pilarski, Michael Ausfelder, Neil Wood, Ross Hopkins, Ally Wright, Lee Valentine, Simon Fisher, Keely Fisher, Ian Bunning, Jack Thorpe, Polly Walker, Jeremy Hoare, Jason Cannon, Andy Waind, Julie Hamill, Mark Ashenden, Paul Myland, Big Sam, Craig Skinner, Lisa Stevens, Mark Wells, Simon Langford, Maddie Sinclair, Kate Park, Sam Copeman, Julie Woolfe, Mark Dyer, Steve Crouch, John Molloy, Ian Ringrose.

AKNOWLEDGEMENTS

Fi – Thanks for your love, support and for laughing at parts of the book, even those bits that aren't meant to be funny! After having to put up with me writing 3 books in the last 4 years, I know I promised not to write any more for a while but I have this idea....

Harrison & Baxter – Read the books that I wrote about The Posh and dedicated to each of you before you read this one. Maybe you can use this book as a reference to "how not to live your teen's and early 20's". Let me know when you are ready to go to Glastonbury – I can't wait to be an embarrassing dad.

Mum & Dad – For the Bowie gig, the Billy Bragg tape and for so much more.

My Sister – For being a pain in the arse & for stopping 'Amy' from killing me at V97.

Doody and Jacko – For being Doody and Jacko. Mine's a London Pride tops & a trip to the offy after a day at Newmarket Races.

To all of the women featured in this story – if you're reading this, I'm sure you have recognised your role in the book, despite me changing the names to protect the innocent. I hope life is sweet for you all.

Ralph – For being an amazingly patient editor and helping me with my addiction to commas. The best parts of writing this book have been sat in the Palmy listening to your stories (which are far funnier than mine). Thanks for signing up to the next one....

Mark – For those teenage years spent listening to Prince and then Dinosaur Jr. If your brother hadn't liked Morrissey, I would never have got into this mess!

All of my mates that feature in the book – Shin, Deano, Ally, Neil, Jake.

Maff – For picking up on the festival line-up mistakes – cheers Screws.

Sinead – For accepting with such good grace that she had to be edited out of the story & for correcting me about 'Friends' catchphrases.

The Pyramid Stage – I haven't been to Glasto since 2007 but it remains my favourite place in the world.

To everyone that pre-ordered the book or who helped promote it on social media. My heartfelt thanks.

Adrian Durham, 'Papa Bear', Laura Dockrill & Julie H – For their kind words that were used in the promotional campaign.

BNBS – For giving the book a chance

Claire – For the brilliant book cover

Tim Burgess – His sparkling 'Telling Stories' was an inspiration & his band remains the greatest live act on the planet.

Billy Bragg – Over 40 gigs, spread over 23 years and still every time I see him, I'm taken back to that amazing first night at Hackney Empire.

Peterborough United – For being an equal purveyor of joy and pain in my life since 1984.

Nye Bevan's statue

First Capital Connect (& subsequently Great Northern) – For providing trains between Peterborough and Kings Cross so slow and often delayed that I had the time to write this book.

The peerless setlist.fm website, which has helped me piece together my fading memories of gigs long past.

Adnams Ghost Ship – For providing the fuel to enable me to dredge up my memories.

And finally to Morrissey. This is my sick way....

Coming in 2016

FAR FROM ME

by Jamie Jones

Jack is 26 and lives happily with his girlfriend, Kirsten, in their one bedroom rented flat in South London. He has never achieved anything he set out to, other than find love.

Kirsten works in marketing and lives life to the full.

They have plans for a bigger flat, children, a joint account and to be married by Elvis in Vegas.

Then Jack goes to Glastonbury and meets Nick.

Follow Jamie 🐦 : @jones_jamie